ONE THOUSAND YEARS
of
EXPLOSIVES

ONE THOUSAND YEARS
of
EXPLOSIVES

From Wildfire to the H-bomb

WILLIAM S. DUTTON

The John C. Winston Company

Library of Congress Catalog Card Number 60-6054

MADE IN THE UNITED STATES OF AMERICA

ACKNOWLEDGMENTS

A portion of a lifetime, many interviews, and extensive reading combined to produce the material for this book. The author is especially indebted to numerous former associates in the Du Pont Company; to the Hercules Powder Company; to the American Chemical Society; to the Hoover Institution on War, Revolution and Peace at Stanford University; to the County Library at Napa, California; and to the following literary sources:

Albion, Robert G., AN INTRODUCTION TO MILITARY HISTORY. Appleton-Century, Inc.

Fuller, Maj. Gen. J.F.C., ARMAMENT AND HISTORY. Charles Scribner's Sons.

Hackett, Francis, HENRY THE EIGHTH. Liveright.

Langer, William L., AN ENCYCLOPEDIA OF WORLD HISTORY. Houghton Mifflin Co.

Lissner, Ivar, THE LIVING PAST. G. P. Putnam's Sons.

Ludwig, Emil, NAPOLEON. Liveright.

Mellor, J. W., A COMPREHENSIVE TREATISE OF INORGANIC AND THEORETICAL CHEMISTRY. Longmans, Green & Co., Inc.

Millis, Walter, ARMS AND MEN. G. P. Putnam's Sons.

Montross, Lynn, WAR THROUGH THE AGES. Harper & Brothers.

Mumford, Lewis, TECHNICS AND CIVILIZATION. Harcourt, Brace & Co.

Neale, J. F., QUEEN ELIZABETH I. Jonathan Cape.

Read, John, EXPLOSIVES. Penguin.

Sohlman, Ragnar, and Schuck, Henrik, NOBEL, DYNAMITE AND PEACE. Cosmopolitan Book Corporation.

Van Gelder, Arthur Pine, and Schlatter, Hugo, HISTORY OF THE EXPLOSIVES INDUSTRY IN AMERICA. Columbia University Press.

BLASTERS' HANDBOOK, 14TH EDITION. The Du Pont Co.

ENCYCLOPAEDIA BRITANNICA, 11TH EDITION.

By the same author

ADVENTURE IN BIG BUSINESS

CONTENTS

Chapter 1

LIGHT IN THE POWDER SMOKE

Turn back the clock if you would weigh man's chances of surviving exploding H-bombs, intercontinental missiles, and rocket barrages from fleets of spaceships. Go back a thousand years to when our modern age, so called, really began.

The ox, the ass, the horse, the camel, even the elephant had been tamed and harnessed, the wheel invented, sails put on ships. The Pyramids of Egypt had been built, the *Iliad* and the *Odyssey* written. The atomic theory, first propounded by the Greek philosopher, Democritus, was already fourteen centuries old.

A million years or more had rolled over mankind, and youth might well have asked what there was left to do. Most of the great deeds seemed to have been done, the big discoveries made, everything worth inventing or within human capability, invented. Seemingly life's pattern was set for another million years.

Then, gunpowder!

Gunpowder set off changes as vast as, if not vaster than, those ever to arise from any other invention, not excepting the wheel or the printing press. It provided the first form of physical energy — power — not found in nature.

The fact that man himself could develop energy by

combining, as in gunpowder, a few ordinary materials, gave a new direction to thinking, one that broke so sharply with the past that today, a millennium later, we are still trying to grasp the enormity of the departure.

Gunpowder led to guns, and over the ten centuries leading to our own, the two recast war and peace, shifted world leadership from the yellow and brown races to the white, and so molded western civilization.

Powder and guns conquered the Americas for the white man, though that conquest — as we may learn by turning back history's clock — was but one scene in the drama of change unfolding from man-developed energy.

For the gun was more than a gun: it was a tool by which explosive energy could be put to work, the fore-runner of the steam engine, gasoline motor, and jet plane. Gunpowder itself was the direct ancestor of nitroglycerin, dynamite, TNT, and the hydrogen bomb — mark the ever-ascending explosive power!

The grim day of Hiroshima's destruction dawned not in World War II but in the pop of the first firecracker, probably before A.D. 1000.

Alfred Nobel, who founded the Nobel Peace Prize on a fortune made in explosives, wrote in 1892 as he neared the end of his life:

> The day when two army corps will be able to destroy each other in one second, all civilized nations will recoil from war in horror and disband their armies.

That day is here, our day. Yet the armies still march.

The search for destroyers ever more terrible goes on. A dazed humanity asks, To what end?

The powder smoke of centuries may hold an answer, for despite our smiles at the ancient adage, history *is* prone to repeat itself.

Gunpowder and each of its explosive progeny was the dreaded H-bomb of its time, the beginning of debacle. The debacles came, thrones and empires crashed, societies perished. But men pushed on to higher goals. The wreckers of the old orders of life blazed the way for new and better ones; the more frightful the explosive threat, the greater mankind's ultimate gain.

Explosives made modern democracy possible. They inspired signal advances in our material sciences, shaped much of our industry. They ushered in the Age of the Common Man, the name by which our age might well become known once historians have appraised its full scope.

The story of explosives is a factual parallel to Robert Louis Stevenson's classic of English fiction, *The Strange Case of Dr. Jekyll and Mr. Hyde.* By day, Dr. Jekyll stood for all that was good; by night, Mr. Hyde symbolized all that was evil. But the two were one, the same man.

But Stevenson's tale ends in tragedy. That the story of explosives could end happily — *should* end happily — is the promise of a thousand years of history.

Explosives did not create war or add to its savagery; both are almost as old as man himself. Explosives did generate such changes in the peaceful pursuits of all civilized peoples that, lacking those changes, every wheel of modern industry would stop and our civilization itself would fade as if it had not been.

We would be back in a bygone world, when life seemed set in an iron mold cast by uncounted dead centuries, and the chances of a plain man's bettering his lot appeared as thin as his purse, which was too often empty.

Chapter 2

A DEMON IS BORN

ABOUT the only thing certain as to gunpowder's origin is that most people of old were convinced — as many still are — that it was an invention of the devil. The authentic records of its discovery are most sketchy.

During the Sung dynasty in ancient China some unknown scribe made this entry in the annals:

> In the first year of the period *Kai-Khing* the spear of the vehement fire *(To-lo-tsi-ang)* was made. A handful of grains was placed in a long bamboo tube and set on fire. A strong flame came out of it and the grains were ejected with a noise similar to that of a *paos,* and scattered to a distance of 150 paces.

The first year of *Kai-Khing* was A.D. 1259, a *paos* was a stone-throwing machine, and the spear of the vehement fire was most likely similar in action to the firework now known as a Roman candle. Undoubtedly the bamboo tube was plugged shut at its base, the powder was poured into it through its open end or muzzle, and the charge was ignited by means of a wick or fuse inserted through a touchhole.

There is evidence that the Chinese had firecrackers, as well as other fireworks, two centuries earlier. As

5

neither of these things could have been made without black gunpowder, or black powder, as the parent of all explosives is called today to distinguish it from smokeless powder, the Chinese seem to have a strong claim to gunpowder's invention about A.D. 1000.

They did not invent guns, though their spark-throwing tube was a step toward them. If they used gunpowder for war at all, it was to awe the enemy by displays of their supposedly magic ability to make noise, flame, and smoke. It was left to the Arabs, then the leaders in world science, to develop *To-lo-tsi-ang* into a tool of death.

Preserved in the Asiatic Museum at Petrograd, Russia, is a fragile and faded Arabian parchment. It presents a sketch, drawn by one Shems Eddin Mohammed in 1304, of a new weapon. The legend describes this as a spear that hurls arrows at the enemy's breast. Again the spear is a bamboo tube, but it has been reinforced by metal bands, obviously to withstand a heavier explosive force. Amid flame and smoke, an arrow is shown flying from the muzzle.

That spear, so called, was probably the first gun — a word that was yet to be coined. Its arrow was the first explosively propelled missile. If so, the device was also the first internal combustion engine.

The fact that this engine had only one cylinder, and it of bamboo, does not alter by an iota the new principle that was introduced to the art of mechanics, a principle which was to place in human hands a source of power vast beyond all dreams. It was the principle that the expanding gases released by any sudden, violent combustion may, *if confined,* be directed toward a vent and put to work.

Touch a spark to loose gunpowder, and usually the powder will merely burn, releasing its escaping gases harmlessly into the atmosphere. Only rarely do the gases detonate or explode, and then by no established rule. Likewise the gas or steam that arises from an open kettle of boiling water vanishes quickly, as a rule, into the air of one's kitchen.

But pack gunpowder into a paper cartridge, or anything that confines it, then apply a spark, and you need have no uncertainty over what will happen: the powder will explode with a bang. Clamp a lid on your boiling kettle of water, and shortly the kettle will burst. Or if the lid is not clamped on too tightly, it will be hurled toward the ceiling in a cloud of steam.

Similar examples might be given for gasoline or dynamite or any other explosive material, including the atom. The point is that they react consistently to fire by exploding only when confined in a manner that prevents the escape of their gases.

The Chinese discovered the explosive potential of gunpowder, probably by accident, and invented firecrackers. In *To-lo-tsi-ang,* they carried their discovery to the stage that might be likened to the open, steaming kettle: that is, they directed the expanding gases of combustion through an open tube to the free air, and so added a fiery display to smoke and noise. The Arabs took the next forward step. By blocking the open part of the tube, after loading it with a wad and an arrow, they formed a chamber in which to confine the gases and build up their pressure. Thus they created an effect analogous to that of the not-too-tightly-clamped lid on a steam kettle.

At that time, of course, nobody thought of gunpowder and steam and gasoline as having the same explosive potentials, or as being governed by the same principle they demonstrated with the first gun, but these facts are obvious on every hand in our modern world.

The modern steam engine is powered by the force of expanding steam trapped in cylinders or tubes of steel, each with its vent. The gasoline motor is run by the gases given off by charges of ignited gasoline, gases that finally escape to the air through an exhaust pipe. Both engines are machine-triggered batteries of firing guns, cousins of the modern machine gun. The engine batteries propel pistons up and down in seesaw motion to turn wheels; the gun battery propels bullets.

The histories of power engines and firearms are intermingled. One of the first inventors to see the relationship between steam and gunpowder was Leonardo da Vinci, the great Italian artist and engineer. He designed a steam cannon. Years later such a cannon was actually built and tested in the American Civil War; it was rejected as too cumbersome. In turn, gunpowder was among the first fuels tried in attempts to build what became automobile and aircraft engines, and steam was a rival candidate.

You must stretch your imagination hard to picture

the Arabs' bamboo tube of 1304 as the ancestor of to-day's space rockets, yet it was. The tube itself, reversed, is now the missile or rocket, and it is now the recoil felt by the Arab marksman that kicks the tube into space. Despite the new magnitude and cost, the principle of combustive gases seeking escape through a vent still rules, and even the chemical composition of the gases is fundamentally unchanged.

Not everybody, however, credits invention of the first gun to the Arabs. The people of Freiburg in Baden, Germany, a city near the French-Swiss border known to American troops of World War II, also have a claimant. To him, a humble monk, they erected a monument in their ancient square, the Franziskaner, and so began a centuries-old argument over facts.

If you wish to believe Freiburg tradition, backed by some real evidence, both gunpowder and guns were invented by Friar Berthold Schwarz, who is described as a worthy and ingenious monk, doctor, and alchemist. Whether or not he performed either of the feats claimed for him is one of history's unsolved mysteries through which the friar moves, a shadow clad in somber gray, poor and scanty of all worldly goods, himself a mystery.

The old Latin records refer to him as Bertholdus Niger, or Black Berthold. Some trace that rather ominous name to the location of Freiburg in the Black Forest, at the foot of the Schlossberg, a hill upon which the ruins of two ancient castles still stand. But skeptics attribute it to Black Berthold's delvings into alchemy, which was regarded as one of the black arts.

Alchemy, the forerunner of modern chemistry, was

an odd blending of magic, sorcery, demonology, fraud, and a genuine devotion to one of the great sciences in its infancy. A main goal of the alchemists was to transmute lead into gold, and some kings who listened to alchemists awoke later with a chest of counterfeit "gold" coins on their hands. As a class, alchemists were linked with bats, dank caves, brimstone. They were accused of stealing dead men from their graves by night, as some undoubtedly did to learn more about the human body.

There is no evidence that Black Berthold robbed either kings or graves, but the accounts of him are queer indeed. One states that he discovered gunpowder in 1259, the year that the Chinese spangled the air with *To-lo-tsi-ang*. A second asserts that he invented the free art of using firearms in the year 1380, 121 years later. Either this shadowy monk was a most precocious infant and a more amazing old man, or the dates of his supposed inventions were badly mixed up.

The mix-up can be explained. The monks, who practiced poverty as a virtue, used the parchments on which they wrote over and over again. Each time, the preceding writing was scraped off with a knife. However, often the old dates and messages continued to show faintly through the fresh writing, which in turn faded over the centuries. For that reason, many of the old parchments which have been passed on to us are like repeatedly used, poorly washed blackboards.

Because of this, and a careful study of the surviving accounts, it is now held that Berthold Schwarz invented a gun or cannon of sorts in 1313. And despite the Arab record of 1304, the partisans of Black Berthold present it as the first firearm.

A fine old copper engraving, a treasure of the University of Ghent in Belgium, memorializes the German monk's exploit in picture and Latin script. Made in 1570, the engraving shows the interior of a cannon foundry of that day. Outside the foundry are sketched a blazing cannon and a fortress crumbling under the bombardment. An inset depicts the "powder monk" at work in his laboratory, flint and steel in hand. On a bench before him a mortar, resembling a big mug, is exploding a block upward into the air, while the wraith of a demon looks on approvingly.

The Latin inscription beneath these grim doings reads: "That thunders and thunderbolts should be brandished in the hand was surely given to us by the powers below."

No longer is the claim that Black Berthold invented the first gunpowder taken seriously, at least outside Freiburg. Meanwhile, over the centuries that city has been battered time and time again by cannon, the origin of which it proudly attributes to the genius of a native son.

Here our story shifts to England and to another friar. Like Berthold Schwarz, he also wears the gray gown and tonsure that marked the Franciscan monks of old. He, too, has dedicated himself to poverty, though not poverty of the mind. That sort of want Friar Roger Bacon condemned throughout a long life, with the result that his name has come down to us as one of the most distinguished connected with the founding of the modern sciences.

Roger Bacon also has a monument. It was erected in the tiny English town of Ilchester in Somersetshire during 1914, the seven hundredth year after his birth there. It is a modest brass tablet set in a wall of St. Mary's, the ancient parish church, and this is its inscription:

> To the Immortal Memory of ROGER BACON, a Franciscan Monk and also a free enquirer after true knowledge. His wonderful powers as mathematician, mechanician, optician, astronomer, chemist, linguist, moralist, physicist, and physician gained him the title of *Doctor Mirabilis*. He first made known the composition of gunpowder, and his researches laid the foundations of modern science. He prophesied the making of machines to propel vessels through the water without sails or oars; of chariots to travel on land without horses or other draught animals; of flying machines to traverse the air. He was imprisoned, starved, and persecuted by the suspicious ignorance of his contemporaries, but a fuller knowledge now acclaims and honours him as one of the greatest of mankind. Born at Ilchester in 1214. Died at Oxford in 1294.

It was Roger Bacon who stripped gunpowder of its magic and mystery by showing that this reputed gift of the devil to men was a mixture of very earthy materials.

The English monk was a graduate of both Oxford University and the University of Paris, then Europe's most respected seat of learning. He studied Latin, Greek, and Arabic — languages he came to know as well as he knew English and French. The works of Aristotle and of Arab scholars convinced him that much of Europe's teaching was a sham or pretense to knowledge and hid vast ignorance.

He attacked sham with a fearless pen. It was his campaign to expose the fraud of the "black art" that led him into alchemy. Some alchemists encouraged the popular belief that they were allied with Satan, for it made more salable the potions they mixed for warding off evil. Bacon, as a monk, was pledged to combat unholy alliances, real or pretended. Besides, he saw that if alchemy was to become a science and a power for good, it had to be freed of fakery and founded on tested truths.

To those ends he began a fiery quest. Incendiary weapons of many kinds, known generally as wildfires, long had been used in warfare, most notably in the Middle East and the Orient. Their composition was shrouded in secrecy. The good friar's cell-workshop must have become a small inferno as he began delving into the methods of producing these fuming, flaming mixtures of war, and looking into their histories. His studies took him back to the wars of the ancient Spartans.

A trick of the Spartans about 400 B.C., he learned, was to soak blocks of wood in hot pitch and sulphur, pile them against the walls of an enemy town, and apply the torch. Town walls were then built of wood, and this simple form of wildfire roasted thousands — until stone walls rose.

Flame throwers, ancestors of the German *Flammenwerfer* of World War I, were invented next.

The original flame thrower was in the form of a huge

iron caldron filled with burning pitch, sulphur, and charcoal. This was mounted atop a high, movable platform which the attackers wheeled up to the defenders' wall. The hollow trunk of a tree was then tilted to the edge of the caldron, and air was pumped through the trunk with an enormous bellows. Thus tarry smoke and tongues of fire were air-blasted upon a luckless enemy.

Century by century the art of fire attack advanced. Petroleum found one of its earliest uses in the wild-fires. All sorts of oils and fats, resin, naphtha, pitch, tar, and turpentine were combined in countless ways. The earth was combed for new incendiary materials, how finely we shall see presently.

Fire pots were invented, and one does not need to try very hard to see in them the primitive forerunner of intercontinental missiles bearing H-bombs. The pots were earthenware jugs of various sizes, some for throwing by hand, like a grenade, others for hurling by catapult. Filled with burning brews and acids to sear the flesh, the jugs burst upon striking and showered their contents. Sometimes, for variety, the chopped-off heads of prisoners were tossed over walls along with the fire pots. At other times, stench-makers were included in the blazing fuel.

The most fiendish and destructive of the fire weapons over which Friar Bacon pondered was Greek fire. Invented by a Greek architect, Greek fire made its bow during the siege of Constantinople by the Moslem Arabs in A.D. 673-678. That city (now Istanbul) was the most heavily fortified city of the Old World, and stood as an impregnable bastion guarding Christian Europe from infidel Asia.

For five years an Arab army and fleet flying the banner of Islam drove their combined might against the city's great series of stone walls and battlements. The stones hurled by the Arab war machines, the flights of arrows that darkened the sun, the terror of the hottest of Arab wildfires left the Christian defenders unmoved. But the siege dragged on. At last Constantinople faced starvation and surrender.

Greek fire turned impending defeat into one of the most amazing victories of military annals.

Long tubes of wood, lined with copper, were mounted on Constantinople's walls. Each tube was connected with a hand-worked pump that could force water through it in the fashion of a fire hose. Tubs held the water — and also some undisclosed mixture.

The next Arabian attack was met by a power that by all standards then existing was other than human. The water that was pumped into the tubes streamed forth as liquid fire — a fire impossible to quench.

Armored Arab warriors were cooked inside their armor; the unarmored were sizzled as if on spits. The liquid fire converted wooden war machines into blazing pyres.

No wildfire known was like this one. Again and again bucket brigades doused it with water; the water acted like fuel poured on the flames. The only escape was flight, and the attackers fled in disorder and terror. Around the city's walls were strewn the charred dead.

Later, Greek ships equipped with the "wet fire"

engines burned the Arab fleet, ending one of history's longest sieges of any city.

Bent on revenge, in A.D. 718, a new generation of Arabs, skeptical of the tales of their fathers, attacked Constantinople by sea. Their fleet was met by a monstrous array. Every Greek ship had on its bow the bronze head of a lion, tiger, or other wild animal. Mouths were wide open, fangs bared. The two fleets drew together, supposedly to fight hand to hand, the usual practice, when the Greek ships backed their oars. From the snarling bronze heads spouted the fire that no water could quench.

Like blazing rain it fell upon the Arab galley slaves chained to their oars. It slithered over wooden decks into every corner and crevice. Every Arab vessel was soon a furnace, while the victorious Greeks pulled away to a safe spot to watch.

Similarly, in A.D. 941 a Russian fleet was destroyed, and in A.D. 1043 a second Russian fleet.

What was this master destroyer?

Certainly, to men who faced it, Greek fire was as terrible a weapon as any that we know today. Moreover, it was a complete mystery. When, 560 years or more after its first use, Roger Bacon began his study of wildfires, the composition of Greek fire was still a secret. No defense had been found against it except to keep beyond range of the fire tubes.

The English friar, now past thirty-five, was one of the ablest men in Europe. He was acquainted with sulphur, the brimstone — "stone that burns" — of many an unholy tale. It was probably one of the ingredients of Greek fire. He knew naphtha, the heavy oil of petroleum, was believed to be another part of the mixture. He was familiar with quicklime, which boils angrily when water is put on it, making it a third suspect.

All of these, modern chemists think, contributed to the phenomenon of Greek fire. But there was something else, an unknown "X."

Was it saltpeter, or niter?

Saltpeter had been identified only recently, Bacon learned as he pored over Arab manuscripts. One writer, Abd Allah, called it Chinese snow, and added that it was a material of lowest origin. The stuff was said to flare fiercely at the touch of a flame and to char wood like a red-hot iron.

Could this be the "magic" behind Chinese fireworks, the missing "X" of Greek fire? The first gun was yet to be fired when Roger Bacon turned his investigations to saltpeter, not dreaming that he was playing with destiny.

The most likely place to find saltpeter in Bacon's England was in a dirty stable, which explained the reference to its low origin. There it was most obvious in the form of an uninviting white scum, resembling mold, on the surface of decaying animal refuse. By washing the refuse with water, then boiling off the water, one might get a handful of saltlike crystals which were saltpeter.

In stables with masonry walls, the crystals often

formed on the walls and could be scraped off with a knife. Saltpeter might also have been recovered from guano left in caves by hordes of bats, or from the rookeries of seafowl along rainless, and so unwashed, coasts. A deposit in South Africa has been attributed to the droppings of untold generations of rock rabbits.

How Friar Bacon got his saltpeter we do not know. From wherever it came, it was a product of nature's ageless process of dust to dust, of the decomposition of the organic wastes and remains of living creatures and plants. We do know, for he emphasized it in his writings, that he recovered it with the utmost care and refined the crystals until they were white, odorless, and tasteless, the last similarity to their origin removed.

He mixed saltpeter with one after another of the materials long used in contriving wildfires. As a rule, whenever the white crystals were added the mixtures burned more violently. It was in combination with sulphur and charcoal, which had been employed more than sixteen hundred years before by the Spartans in their flame thrower, that the results were the most startling.

He never did learn — nor has anybody since — the secret of Greek fire. He did better: he discovered a destroyer that was to blast Greek fire into obscurity.

In the year of 1242, Friar Bacon inscribed his find on parchment in churchly Latin. He wrote that if three materials, and only three among the many he had tried, were properly wetted, ground, and mixed, and the mixture was ignited by a flame or spark, "you will produce a thundering noise and a bright flash, if you know the 'trick.' "

The materials were saltpeter, sulphur, and charcoal, by-products, respectively, of dung heaps, volcanoes, and charred wood. Joined, these became a powder colored black by the charcoal. That black powder was the first explosive — gunpowder — to be made in the Christian world.

The trick, as Bacon called it, was in knowing how to transform this powder into a disruptive force by which, he wrote, an army "might be either blown up bodily or put to flight by the terror caused by the explosion." Gunpowder's force consisted in confining the combustion and compressing the escaping gases, as the Arabs were to do in their metal-bound tube sixty-five years later.

Friar Bacon did not carry his work so far as to construct firearms, but it is probable that he made and exploded the first bomb, though his writings do not mention it. They do make clear that he foresaw in black powder a means by which men might do enormous evil. For that reason he sought to keep full details of his work from the mass of people, or what he termed the crowd. As he wrote later, he feared that the crowd would misuse this new power "to its own detriment and that of the wise."

Hoping to avoid such misuse, he gave the formula for black powder in a Latin cryptogram which he thought only the wisest men would be able to decipher. He thought rightly, for his cryptogram remained an unsolved puzzle for 662 years, when a British colonel unraveled it. However, Bacon openly told of his use of saltpeter, and so made his puzzle defeat its aim.

You may mix ground sulphur and charcoal with saltpeter in almost any proportions, and the compound will be explosive if confined. Saltpeter is the explosive key, the trigger.

Once that secret was out, the whitish scum of stables, caves, and rookeries became more sought after than diamonds or gold. Saltpeter was to vie with the printing press in shaping civilization until our own century.

Nowadays great chemical plants, aglitter with stainless steel and working ceaselessly day and night, supply us with a modern counterpart of saltpeter by trainloads and shiploads. The process, a triumph of modern chemical science, goes by the name of atmospheric nitrogen fixation. We shall see how it evolved as we follow gunpowder's march. It is enough now to explain that the great plants capture nitrogen from the air and "fix" it — that is, hold it in usable form — by imprisoning its molecules as a liquid or a powderlike solid.

So captured, nitrogen helps fertilize all crops and is indispensable in making many kinds of plastics, textiles such as nylon, the newest of explosives, and scores of other things in daily use.

Fortunes have been spent to make the nitrogen fixation plants stand out as dazzling achievements of today's chemical genius, which they are. But sniff inside: you will smell ammonia, the same pungent odor that Bacon smelled in the stables.

Humbly, with much less fuss and cost, in those stables nature fixed nitrogen in saltpeter. It was the nitrogen that made its lowly carrier more valuable to men than any precious metal.

Who first discovered saltpeter's unique properties remains a mystery of the ages. The ancient alchemists knew nothing of nitrogen as such, though it was a part of every breath they took. However, there on stable walls for all to see were the saltlike crystals. Every tiller of the soil knew that manure, when it produced those crystals and smelled of ammonia, possessed an unusual power. Plowed into farm fields, it made all crops grow taller.

Perhaps an old alchemist, seeking to turn lead into gold, looked for the secret in those crystals. A brewer of evil potions might have scraped some from the wall of a bat cavern. Plain curiosity may have inspired another researcher to experiment with them. Whatever was true, at some unmarked milestone along progress's road an unsung prober gathered some saltpeter and mixed it with carbon or wood pulp. To this mixture, by intent or by accident, he touched fire. Instantly, the crystals blazed angrily. Their fixed nitrogen reverted to its free gaseous form, burst the shackles that bound its molecules to those of oxygen, and both elements returned to the air, all in a split second.

Nitrogen is the rebel of the elements. It makes up

four-fifths of the atmosphere. Its urge to return to the air when it is held captive, or fixed, far exceeds the freedom urge of the wildest grizzly bear. Ever seeking to escape when held captive in trees, plants, people, or explosives of all kinds, ever pulling toward the sun which provides its energy, it is the detonator of all growth.

The making of world revolution exploded in the English monk's cell when he put brimstone and charred wood into the pot with saltpeter and flicked a spark from his flint upon them.

Chapter 3

THE MAILED RIDER

No other part of the globe was to be so completely changed by gunpowder as Roger Bacon's own Europe during the next several centuries. The established civilization, older than our own, was to be destroyed and replaced by another. The new was to form the foundation of our Western civilization of today.

Knowing what gunpowder destroyed is as important to our theme as knowing how the destruction came about, if we are to judge whether the change was for the better or worse. So let us look swiftly at Europe as it was before gunpowder.

If you had a title of nobility, a castle, and a private army you might have done very well for yourself in that Europe of sword, bow, spear, and catapult; of windmill, water wheel, and muscle power. Few people could read or write or hope to learn: that was left to the privileged, to men of the church, hired scribes, soothsayers, astrologers, alchemists. Those who showed too much curiosity over the unknown laid themselves open to charges of witchcraft and might be jailed or burned at the stake. Roger Bacon, monk though he was, spent twenty-four years in prison.

The vast bulk of the people worked on land that they did not own, and performed menial labor as serfs or little better for their overlords. They owned only what they wore on their backs, and it was humble cloth.

The road to honor, fame, and wealth was the road of the armored and plumed fighting man on horseback. He owned the countryside and the grim castle that guarded it. All men in his fief were his vassals. He made the laws and was judge and jury. A man could be hanged for stealing so small a sum as a dollar.

Property was valued above life. A good pig was worth more than its keeper. When a common man died in battle — and all men on foot were regarded as common — nobody bothered to count the loss; it was deemed too trifling.

Such was feudalism, the plan of government in the Europe of Roger Bacon and Black Berthold. Feudalism had grown to dominance as a consequence of the breaking up of the Roman Empire two centuries earlier. When Rome's legions marched out, the police power marched with them. Disorder, pillage, and murder marched in. The remnants of government left in the hands of native kings were too weakly organized to restore order; it was a case of everybody for himself.

The owners of small farms and other property went to their stronger neighbors, the owners of castles who commanded men-at-arms, for protection against the roving bands of looters that sprang up everywhere. The price of protection was surrender of all property and rights to the strong neighbor. A further fee was complete subservience to the despot of the district, and service under his banner whenever he chose to make war.

Thus strong men gained possession of provinces. They could muster their own armies and declare war at will. They had neither to pay nor feed and clothe their impressed fighters. Every soldier and subcommander was expected to provide for himself by looting the country through which the army moved.

It was a ragged, undrilled, undisciplined horde—the portion of the feudal army that was afoot. Each man wore the garb of farm or shop; uniforms were unknown. The masters of the fiefs, lesser lords, and knights on horseback, however, glittered in a splendor unrivaled by ancient Bagdad.

Most of Europe's kings, especially those of Germany and France, were heavily dependent on the military might of the great landlords, and did everything to please them. The strong men were showered with royal favors and raised to noble rank or made knights. Their land seizures were given the stamp of legality. Their titles of nobility, castles, and lands were made hereditary. The feudal dukes, marquises, counts, earls, lords, and barons so appointed became an aristocracy before which Europe's people were to humble themselves for centuries to come.

The noble houses adopted flags individual to their owners, and it was these banners that the retainers followed into battle. The national flags which we know today were yet to be evolved.

The castles guarding the great landholdings grew in

size and strength with the rise of the feudal lords' power. Situated in spots hard to attack, atop hills, on cliffs, on islands in lakes or rivers, at times surrounded by swamps, the heavy stone walls, bastions, and towers of these private forts defied capture by any weapons then known. Rocks hurled by catapult and similar war machines bounced off the castle's lofty sides. Stone parapets shielded the defenders from the iron bolts of crossbows and from arrows. As a rule, the well-defended castle could only be starved into surrender, and it was kept too well provisioned to invite so long and costly an effort to take it.

Social progress had thus entered a dead-end street. Encased in splendid armor, astride his mighty war horse, the lord of the area, enriched by his tenants, was impregnable against any ordinary attack by ordinary men. His castle stronghold was equally impregnable. From its high ramparts, the drawbridge drawn, the local despot could defy kings and often did. And he defied all change not to his liking.

War was the golden road to glory, the one calling to which youth could look for name, fame, and fun. It is not strange, inasmuch as the lords dictated all terms, that war became a kind of sport, that battles were won or lost in a way to expose the feudal lords to a minimum risk of getting killed.

The battle of Bouvines, named for that village near the French-Belgian border, presents a good example of the prevailing rules of war. Fought in July of 1214, the battle is described as a typical one during the

Middle Ages. The king of France and his feudal lords, with their vassals, opposed the king of England and much of the power of Holland, Belgium, and Germany. These are modern designations: the nations as we know them today were still in embryo, their lands still belonging to feudal princes, dukes, and counts.

All told, some 13,500 horsemen and 70,000 footmen were in the two armies. Naturally, the horsemen were noblemen, knights, and gentlemen, for lesser men did not ride horses.

The fray lasted all day. According to the best accounts, the foot soldiers were one great mass in the center armed in the main with pikes and crossbows, and many thousands of them were killed on both sides. In that terse summary, history disposes of the rabble whose blood reddened the field.

But carefully compiled figures and names tell us what happened among the men on horseback. The French knights, then rated as the best mailed horsemen in Europe, wound up the day without a man killed or captured. The English and their allies lost the battle, and 170 of their knights were slain. Three counts, twenty-five barons, and more than one hundred knights were captured by the French.

The death of 170 knights among 13,500 horsemen in an all-day battle is cited as an unusually heavy casualty list. It can be explained only by the stubbornness of the English knights who refused to surrender.

Capture of a king was the high goal, with princes, dukes, counts, barons, and knights rating as prizes in that order. Ransoms in money and goods could be asked for them. The captured noble's vassals paid the ransom, though it reduced them to their last penny.

Any local strong man who grew bored by peace or envied a neighbor's landholdings, or whose treasury needed fattening by plunder, could start a war. By promising his vassals all the loot they could carry home, after he had taken his share, the warmaker never lacked recruits. Kings warred against kings, as well as against nobles who coveted their crowns. Barbarian hordes from Asia overran Europe in periodic sprees.

By 1300, war was a leading industry of western civilization, the chief aristocratic occupation. Even churchmen maintained their private armies.

You may still see in Europe the relics of this war industry. The richer towns and cities surrounded themselves with moats and great defensive walls, many of which still stand. In villages the houses and stables of peasants were built wall to wall for better defense. Convents and monasteries became hilltop strongholds. The castles of the robber barons, one name by which history knows them, commanded every fertile valley.

Out of this industry dedicated to war and plunder emerged a most unusual business unit, the free company.

The free company was a fighting unit, at times as large as a small army, that sold its services to the highest bidder — a city or town, rich merchant, prince, or king, or whomever it chose to favor. Its leader was a captain of renown who pledged allegiance to nobody, except by contract. This practice led to the name *condottieri,* or contractors. The company's officers were men-at-arms who also held their lances to be free of any lord's dictates. Our modern term, "free lance," applied mainly to writers or professional people who are attached to no payroll, is derived from these times.

Free companies of Swiss were hired as defenders of the Pope, and the Swiss Guard still does duty at the Vatican in Rome. Adventure-loving Irish, Scots, Belgians, and Germans won high fame in free companies, doing much of the fighting for the kings of England and France in their Hundred Years War of 1337 to 1453.

The sword was more than a weapon in pre-gunpowder Europe. It was a symbol of rank. Only nobles, knights, and gentlemen by birth were permitted to wear a sword. A commoner who carried one was deemed as wrong as any plain soldier today who impersonates an officer.

Most of Europe was in feudalism's grip when Roger Bacon happened upon gunpowder, and it would have been astonishing, indeed, had the lords of the land welcomed any discovery that held a threat to their estate. Their power was secure as long as no new weapon appeared to destroy it. The fact that nobility had been made hereditary also made serfdom and low estate hereditary to working millions. A limited few were born to ride, all others to walk.

It had not always been so, which was an added reason why the feudal lords opposed any change. Once, both the Greeks and the Romans had glorified the foot soldier. That had been when the spirit of republicanism had ruled, when even the great were not too proud to fight afoot. It was before the invention of the saddle and stirrups, and before bloody Adrianople, in A.D. 378. At that epic battle, wild Gothic horsemen had routed the Roman legions, slain the Roman emperor, and raised to power the man on horseback for the next thousand years.

The power and glamor of the horseman had ascended with the gradual development of complete armor for man and beast, for only the rich could afford both armor and horse. Next, castle building, which required more wealth, had elevated the very rich to the roles of minor gods.

Why change, indeed!

To the mailed rider, safe against ordinary arrows, the invention of a weapon so formidable as the crossbow had been threat enough. This, a cumbersome bow of iron which the bowman bent by turning a windlass, hurled iron bolts that were about ten inches long. The bolts could kill or mutilate horribly.

To withstand such missiles, armored men had been forced to add to the weight of their armor and of the padding inside. On a hot day the heavily padded iron casings became like ovens in which the wearer baked.

The feudal lords denounced the crossbow as an atrocity of Asiatic barbarians, as a weapon of lowborn cowards afraid to fight face to face like men. It was condemned as a menace to civilized society. In 1139 the highest council of the church declared the crossbow an inhuman weapon that was "unfit for Christian use."

Now note an odd twist of destiny. The free companies, to whom war was a business, eagerly adopted the crossbow. Foot soldiers were hired and trained in its use. In defiance of all tradition, some crossbowmen were put on horses.

Kings, too, were now more businesslike, not hesitating to use poison or a knife in the dark to rid the kingdom of objectionable rivals. Kings became the chief employers of the free companies and their bolt hurlers.

This royal catering to commoners armed with a weapon that might unhorse a duke was like seeding the clouds of a gathering storm. It seems that the kings failed to grasp the possibility that anything capable of unhorsing a duke might also unthrone a king at some later day.

The clouds grew heavier with disclosure of the secret of gunpowder. Here was a potential weapon that might blast the most costly armor into scrap, the strongest castle into rubble. Methods for employing the explosive in war were yet to be worked out, guns to be developed; the demon was still to be shackled, but there it was, both a threat and a challenge to the bold.

Again, it was the adventurers of the free companies, fearing neither man nor devil, who took up the challenge. What if this thunder-making powder was of the blackest origin? So was war! Besides, the contractor who offered gunpowder's might for sale could surely command fatter contracts.

The first crude cannon were cast of brass, by whom we do not know. Gunners learned how to load the brass monsters and ignite the explosive charge. Nobody bothered to note how many of them were blown to bits in these tests, but it is a good guess that more cannon blew up in the trials than survived to roar at an enemy. These pioneer guns were shaped like huge flower vases with narrow necks which formed the muzzle. The French named them *pots de fer,* or fire pots. Their first missiles were arrows, like the Arabs' fire spear of bamboo. Round stones were soon substituted; iron balls came much later.

An ironic destiny still ruled. It was a king, Edward III of England, young, fearless, deaf to his shocked councilors, who was among the first to hire cannoneers. An even dozen of the new craftsmen, probably enough to man two guns, were put on the royal payroll in 1344. To feudal lords, the king's action was akin to hiring hangmen.

Meanwhile, a weapon more deadly than either the crossbow or the first clumsy cannon had been added to England's arsenal. It was the longbow, developed in Wales. A bow of yew wood or elm from five to six feet in length, the new weapon could hurl a yard-long steel-headed arrow through two layers of mail. A good bowman could get off twenty aimed arrows in a minute.

The longbow's arrows became the rain, the cannon's blasts the lightning and thunder of the storm that was now about to break over Europe's feudalism in ever-mounting fury.

Let us, as the storm pends, look quickly over the England of Edward III. It was a product of the Norman Conquest of some three hundred years earlier. Out of the conquest by the French feudal duke, William of Normandy, had risen a new people, and the first strong central government since the Romans had left. The strength was not accidental.

Upon making himself England's king, the Norman conqueror had seized all feudal fiefs and redistributed them among Norman nobles who swore allegiance to him. He carefully kept, however, the best lands for the crown, which made the crown the most powerful force in the kingdom. Private wars were prohibited. New castles could be built only by royal permit.

William and his successors recognized that the kingdom's main strength was in its people, not the feudal lords and barons. Men were allowed to buy their freedom from the landlords and even to own property. A class of yeomen arose who were permitted to offer their services for hire as freemen. The country squire — an eight-ox farmer with 120 lush acres — formed the solid backbone of a growing middle class. Some commoners were raised to knighthood and the nobility, a sharp break from Europe's rule that only those of gentle birth should be ennobled.

When Edward III came to the throne, democracy was planting its roots deep in the Anglo-Saxon countryside. The English freeholder walked his acres, and the free townsman his streets, with head up. By royal decree, every freeman owned a longbow and at least forty good arrows. The longbow was the mark of his freedom, a symbol that vied with the sword!

In 1346, Edward III led into France a most unusual army, a far departure from any army assembled by feudal lords. From the greatest knight down to the lowest stableboy, every soldier was paid a daily wage. He might also share in the plunder. Bowmen and other foot soldiers received wages at least as good as those of a laborer in civil life. Every man, moreover, was a freeman, trained and disciplined; every officer was loyal to the throne. No serf or feudal lord had been called to fight.

The main body of troops was made up of 11,000 English longbowmen, 5000 Welsh pikemen, and 3900 mounted men-at-arms, among them many a squire as proud as any of the knights and barons. Even the cannoneers, their awkward brass fire pots mounted on ox-drawn sleds, were English by birth, which made this a true national army.

It would be nice to be able to say that this invasion of a neighbor was for a noble cause, but it was not. Edward made a dubious claim to the French throne his excuse for the war; its real purpose was plunder. Also, it might enhance our tale if we could say that the cannon were weapons at which the soldiers marveled; the fact is that they were treated as a joke by bowmen and knights alike. Dragged on sleds, mired in mud, their gunpowder often too wet to fire, the clumsy little cannon played so unglorious a role in the invasion that some accounts do not mention them at all.

The English force raided almost unopposed through Normandy and to the very gates of Paris. The summer was well along, the carts heavy with booty, before the French king, Philip of Valois, sent Edward the customary feudal notice that he was leading his own army against the invaders.

On August 26, 1346, Edward formed his army for battle on a well-chosen hillside near the town of Crécy, a name that is important in English schoolbooks. His longbowmen were the heart and the wings of his battle line, and a company of them was placed in reserve in a good shooting position well up the hill. For the first time in many a year the armored knights were treated as a secondary force; a number were ordered to dismount and fight on foot. The old records fail to state where Edward put his cannoneers.

His troops in position, the English king climbed into the tower of a windmill near his army's center. From there he viewed the fighting and issued orders through aides. Again by this act he broke with tradition, which held that a king should be among his sword wielders.

The French straggled into position 60,000 strong against England's 19,900. Philip had 12,000 men-at-arms on horseback, the usual levies of vassals on foot, and 6000 hired crossbowmen from Genoa, Italy. It took Philip's troops most of the day to get into position while the English patiently waited.

At last, in late afternoon, the Genoese crossbowmen opened the battle with a volley of bolts at about two hundred paces. From the hillside, like a gale, burst the

rain of answering arrows from eleven thousand longbows, each arrow aimed to kill.

The crossbowmen reeled and rallied, but the English
arrows kept coming six to every crossbow bolt. The
Genoese were but hired men; they broke in panic.
Perhaps the bang and smoke of one of the English
cannon heightened the panic; the accounts fail to say,
for this was the longbow's day.

As yet beyond range, the French knights saw the
panic in rising fury. There were cries of "Treason!"
One armored rider spurred his charger into the rabble
of hirelings, his sword clearing a path. Pointing his
lance toward the English line, he swung his war horse
into the charge. Behind him in waves of mailed riders,
pointed lances, and dancing plumes charged the French
knights. The dead and wounded Genoese were tram-
pled under the pounding hooves.

The rhythm of the English arrows did not change.
Now the barbed shafts were aimed at the knights'
visors, and helmets were pinned to heads they were
worn to protect. Horses went down, arrows in their
bellies. Only a handful of riders gained the English
line, to die there.

The French horsemen re-formed, stirrup to stirrup,
charged again. They ignored the enemy foot soldiers
in the hope of coming within sword's reach of their
feudal equals, the English knights. But the longbows
knew no social distinctions.

Sixteen times the French elite stormed the English

line. They might have been riding against the cliffs of
Dover. In desperation, a last charge was led by John,
King of Bohemia, there as a French ally. He was one
of Europe's most famous warriors. Six years before, he
had been blinded in battle; now in his fiftieth year, he
invited death in the hope that his example might turn
the day for France.

The blind king had his horse reined to the bridles
of two horses on either side of him, and the three
armored riders charged together. But the day was spent,
it was growing dark, and the men with the longbows
wanted to get to their mess kettles. The King of
Bohemia, an emperor's son, went down among the
French dead, a longbow arrow fired by a commoner
protruding from a chink in his armor.

At midnight Edward's heralds reported to him the
toll of Crécy. The French losses in slain were 1542
lords and knights, uncounted thousands of crossbowmen and lesser foot soldiers. The English lost two
knights, a squire, forty archers, and thirty-six Welsh
pikemen.

Somewhere in the night, Philip of Valois, his army
in flight, knocked at the door of a monastery of the
countryside.

"Who is there?" asked a sleepy monk holding up a
torch.

A tired, beaten voice answered: "The fortune of
France."

The king might have spoken for all of feudalism's

lords on horseback, for their fortune that night was as low as his own. The longbows' arrows, fired by freemen, had sung feudalism's pending doom.

And two funny little brass guns also had spoken at Crécy. Not alarmingly, because it took a lot of time to load them. They were harder yet to aim, and a thunder shower just before the battle had wet most of their powder. But gunpowder had become a weapon! Given time, it was to make even the mighty longbow a toy and turn castles into relics or ruins.

Chapter 4

GUNPOWDER MARCHES

During the siege of the French port of Calais, captured by the English in 1347, Edward III's cannon boomed loudly enough to inspire a poem, preserved in Percy's *Reliques of Ancient English Poetry:*

> Gonners to shew their art
> Into the town in many a parte
>   Schot many a fulle great stone.
> Thanked be God and Mary mild,
> They hurt neyther man, woman nor child;
>   To the houses, though, they did harm.

England's armament now also included an ancestor of the modern machine gun. Several small iron tubes were bound together in a way that enabled the gunner with his match to fire all in a single blast. Later, a French inventor contrived a gun with 144 barrels, so grouped that each set of twelve barrels could be fired as a unit. It required four horses to drag this monster.

By 1400 iron cannon, bound with iron hoops to keep them from bursting, and iron cannon balls were coming into use. An ancient "bombard" that fired balls bigger than watermelons is still preserved at Ghent, Belgium. A handgun had been invented: a tiny cannon, weighing about ten pounds, which fired lead balls. One man could carry it, mount it on a stand, aim in the enemy's direction, and score possibly one hit in ten shots, if his gun did not burst first.

Military men wedded to the chivalrous tradition of looking the enemy in the eye at sword's length denounced these Satanic devices. As Don Quixote, fiction's most ardent supporter of knightly gallantry, said: What was the art of war coming to when a base cowardly hand might take the life of the bravest gentleman by means of a chance bullet coming nobody knows how or from whence? The church railed at this demonry. All decent people were horrified.

But daredevils grasped a golden opportunity. A craft of gunners, which jealously guarded its secrets, sprang up all over Europe. Foundries turned out guns by night. Adventurers organized groups that offered cannon and crews for hire to anybody who wanted a city wall blasted down or a castle door opened. Master gunners became honored rogues, attended by servants and sought by kings.

Ruffians who did not mind dirt were employed to operate saltpeter houses. These were smelly sheds, swarming with flies, in which straw was bedded with garbage, butchers' scraps, and human organic wastes. At a time when the gutters of city streets were open sewers, the stench of the saltpeter houses provoked no popular outcry.

There was little of science and less of good sense in this early march of gunpowder. Friar Bacon had warned that in mixing the sulphur, charcoal, and salt-peter, the powders should be wetted with water to form a cake, which then was ground. Incredibly, the powders were mixed *dry* for almost two hundred years, and countless mixers were blown into eternity.

The dry mix tended to separate under the jolting of transport to the battlefield, so that no gunner was sure his gun would fire when he applied match to touchhole. To overcome that fault, it became a usual practice to mix the gunpowder on the battlefield beside the guns, which was the worst spot that could possibly be chosen. Any spark made by an arrow or crossbolt striking the gun might cause the loose gunpowder to flare like ignited gasoline. An added hazard was the gunner's "match" — a cotton or hemp cord soaked in wine or saltpeter — which was kept lighted to save re-lighting with flint and steel. Many gunners wore the lighted cord about their necks, its sizzling end swinging as they worked.

Perhaps the least understandable phase of this harum-scarum business, which literally boomed, was that nobody as yet had conceived the idea of mounting cannon on wheels. The cumbersome guns, loaded on sleds, were dragged by beasts and men over roads that we today would rate as cow paths. When forced to retreat, an army usually abandoned its guns to the enemy.

Then evolved a military miracle, a major milepost along gunpowder's march.

Our scene shifts to Bohemia, in central Europe. Today one of three provinces of Czechoslovakia, Bohemia in 1400 was a feudal bailiwick that was almost wholly owned and dominated by Germans. It bore its full burden of feudalism's abuses. Czech peasants worked the lands as serfs.

The king, Wenceslaus, was the son of a late German king. He owed allegiance not to the Czech people, but to his brother, Sigismund, Emperor of the Holy Roman Empire. That federation of Europe's larger states, founded by a German ruler in A.D. 962, was now in effect a German superstate.

Most Czechs disliked everything German. Stirring, too, among the landless peasants, lesser gentry, and students were the angry mutterings that would lead to the Protestant revolution led by Martin Luther. At Prague, the capital, the sermons of John Huss were warnings of unrest.

In 1415 Huss was burned at the stake at the German town of Gottlieben. The Czech tempers boiled over into civil war.

The Hussites, as the rebels became known first, were largely landless peasants and leaderless until 1419. On a July morning of that year a Hussite procession which included women and children was passing Prague's Town Hall when stones were hurled from the upper windows. The burgomaster and his councilors could be seen urging on the hurlers.

From the crowd on the street emerged a bearded man who wore a black patch over one eye. His sword, plumed hat, and spurred boots marked him as a soldier of the Czech gentry. Several grim companions strode with him, and were only a step behind as he leaped up the Town Hall's broad stone entranceway, three stairs at a time. Minutes later, the burgomaster was pitched from an upper window to the pavement below. The members of his council came next, one by one.

Hussite peasants killed the officials with their bare hands. The bodies were tossed into the gutter. Then the peasants marched on again, and with them marched Jan Zizka, the bearded man. The landless were leaderless no longer.

When Wenceslaus, the king, got the news, his rage brought on an apoplectic fit during which he died. Everywhere in Bohemia the peasants took up scythes, flails, hay forks, any tool or club that might crack a head, and began driving Germans from the land.

The Emperor Sigismund declared the crown of Bohemia had become his. His brother had died without an heir. He called for total destruction of the Hussites, and an avenging feudal army began forming in Germany under Sigismund's banner.

Hussites who owned something, and had it to lose, urged no resistance. Led by Jan Zizka, the landless peasants chose to fight. They staked their camp on an inaccessible hill in a forest. The place was named Tabor, so they took the new name of Taborites.

Under the one good eye of Jan Zizka, the rebels gathered beneath the trees: men, women, children; the sick, the lame, the old — in all 25,000 strong. Surely it was one of the humblest arrays ever to pose as an army. They took council and announced: "In this hour of vengeance, it behooves us neither to show pity nor imitate the mercy of Jesus. For these are the days of fury, of fervor, and of violence."

Three captains were elected to serve with Jan Zizka, and so began one of the most incredible of wars.

No Czech was better fitted to those days than was the bearded chief in command. Accounts of his early life vary: one says that he had been a chamberlain of the Bohemian court and had lost his eye during a civil war; another, that he was a veteran soldier of sixty-five who had spent most of his years fighting as a free lance for one cause or another in Poland. The second version appears the more likely, because Zizka was no courtier. He knew weapons from battle-axes to crossbows. He was familiar with gunpowder and had his own ideas on how to use it, ideas that as yet nobody had tried. At one time he had fought the Tartars, as well as the Cossacks of Russia.

The strong arm of the veteran soldier is evident in what followed in the Tabor woods. The able-bodied men were organized into a combat force in which each group and company was led by its ablest fighting leaders. This was a radical break from the feudal practice of choosing leaders by the grade of their birth or position. The Taborites ceased to be an unguided mob.

The stronger women and old men were trained in the building of fortifications such as trenches and barricades made out of whatever material was at hand. Again, this broke from the current rule of using body armor and stone walls as defenses against swords, pike, and arrows. The older children were taught to carry ammunition and to serve as messengers. The older women and men were made cooks, the tenders of baggage, the general chore-doers of the army.

Results of the long hours of drilling were tested at night after the moon had tipped the forest's rim. Then, in shadowy groups that came and passed like the wind, the fighters-in-the-making raided the country for miles about.

These forays were for more than practice warfare, however. It was a poor sunrise when the raiders did not return to their hill stronghold with things needed to build an army: horses, oxen, wagons, clothing, food, crossbows, and pikes. Occasionally the plunder included gold and jewels.

With the gold and jewels, old soldier Zizka bought handguns and cannon, shot and gunpowder. He knew the devious ways by which such things could be procured. Besides, Bohemia was peppered with anti-German friends. As the spring of 1420 became summer and the roads were dry, the Taborites moved from their stronghold in force. No longer were they peasants. To the last child, woman, and old man they were soldiers. Their heads were high. No leader held himself to be above those whom he led.

No army like it had ever marched before anywhere. Horsemen fanned ahead as scouts, guarded the flanks, and sealed the rear. When in battle formation, the cavalry was divided into two wings of shock troops which poured into action as the enemy began to break. Thus the man on horseback became an auxiliary, and the spotlight swung toward a new star, the man on foot.

But on the march, the man on foot rode with the best. Jan Zizka put almost his entire army on wheels or horses. Only the tenders of the ox teams strode beside their beasts, and then just until fresh captures could replace the ox teams with horses, even in the baggage train. That train, moreover, was reduced to the barest essentials. Speed of movement was Zizka's aim, a speed that would astound and overwhelm.

For the first time, the clumsy cannon were put on wheels — not on gun carriages, which came much later, but on stout, four-wheeled farm carts. Recoil devices to absorb the back-thrust of a firing gun had to be invented before cannon could go into battle on wheels of their own. Zizka's carts bridged the gap.

The one-eyed veteran's supreme stroke was the *Wagenburg* or wagon-fort. The Tartars and Russians long had used wheeled forts manned by bowmen, but once more Zizka made history. He armor-plated his wagons, pierced the iron sides with loopholes, ten to a mobile fort, and at each loophole put a handgunner. Ten pikemen complemented the ten gunners to defend them against attack while they loaded their guns with ramrod and powder pourer.

The wagon-fort was the first armored war tank.

In June Emperor Sigismund's army besieged Prague. Led by German princes, it was the usual feudal horde of armored barons and knights, menials on foot, hired cannoneers and crossbowmen, adventurers drawn from all over Europe by the prospect of loot. Prague was defended by its people, by free companies hastily hired, and by seven thousand Taborites.

The Taborites occupied a hill that was the key to victory or defeat, depending on who held it. Zizka placed his wagon-forts in the center of his battle line and linked them together with chains so that they would stand as one. At intervals between the forts he dismounted his cannon, each behind an earthen breastwork. His mounted peasants formed the little army's wings.

On July 14th Sigismund's great army moved forward in a general attack. The chief objective was destruction of the Taborite rebels, and the main body of German knights was hurled at Zizka's position. To the princes and barons it was inconceivable that mere serfs would dare to defy such a display of their masters' might.

Up the hill, pennants and plumes streaming, the hooves of war horses thundering, the sun gleaming on spotless armor and swords and lance points, charged the pride and glory of German feudalism. Centuries had gone into molding the riders, and they considered themselves the champions of a way of life that was enduring.

In the wagon-forts, behind the breastworks, on their raid-captured horses, the peasants and Jan Zizka waited, the outlawed and the condemned. They waited, singing a battle hymn. Then the hill itself seemed to explode as the gunners applied their match cords to touchholes. Amid the guns' flashes and the mighty roar, a dense cloud of gunpowder smoke enveloped the Taborite line. The oncoming German war horses reared in terror; many went down with their steel-clad riders in a din of crashing armor and cries of men and animals torn by iron balls, stones, and lead shot.

Again the hymn was heard. The singing rose to a wild surge as Jan Zizka and his peasant horsemen burst from both Taborite wings and piled headlong into the broken and confused melee of horses and knights. The hill was soon cleared of Germans except the dead.

There was no second attack, and that night Sigismund's army drew back from Prague. The hill of the peasants' victory is today a suburb of the old Czech city and is known as Zizkoz after the leader who baptized its soil in enemy blood.

With Prague safe, the Taborites wheeled back to Tabor. During the fall and winter of 1420 and 1421, they raided at will, ranging into German Saxony and Bavaria, and into Austria and Hungary where Sigismund was also king.

In 1421, Sigismund threw a second army against them on the Bohemian border. The Germans are said to have numbered 200,000 against Zizka's 40,000 — his following had grown. In four days the one-eyed captain won two pitched battles, captured two fortified towns, and sent the Emperor Sigismund scurrying back to a safer part of Europe.

Zizka himself lost his second eye. Totally blind, he continued to lead, and wherever the Taborite guns spoke he was close by. His army on wheels kept rolling to wherever a German baron held forth, piling victory upon victory.

Three new armies, assembled by the German princes in turn, were battered into flight by Zizka's guns almost before they were well warmed up. Thereafter, the mere sound of the approaching wagon-forts and cannon-toting carts — a sound that was always accompanied by the singing of battle hymns — was sufficient to turn the German knights into a fugitive mob.

In 1424, Jan Zizka died of illness. According to Czech legend, his skin was dried and made into a drumhead so that his spirit could continue to beat against his German foes.

The Hussite Wars, as history calls them, lasted fourteen years. The peasant rebels and their wheeled guns won some fifty battles and sacked at least five hundred walled towns, monasteries, and feudal castles. They were never defeated until dissension arose in their own ranks. Then one of Zizka's old lieutenants and his men went over to the enemy. The Germans were quick to make use of their knowledge and re-equipped in Zizka fashion. Presently wagon-forts faced wagon-forts, cannon faced cannon, and it was the Germans who had more of each. At the battle of Lipany, in 1434, the Czechs lost eighteen thousand men as well as their cause.

Bohemia returned to German rule. Not, however, without concessions to its peasants. They were recognized at least as people, not as beasts of burden. Neither in Bohemia nor anywhere else in Europe was life ever to be quite the same as it had been. The Hussite wars had awakened all thinking men to a singular fact: The humblest serf with a gun was as big a man as the proudest lord with a sword. The British historian, Thomas Carlyle, aptly summed up that turning point in history: "Gunpowder made all men tall."

It also made the strongest castle and mightiest city walls so much waste masonry. If any doubt remained of that truth, the clinching proof of it was not long in coming. It was supplied by feudal Europe's most hated enemies, the Ottoman Turks.

The Turks, too, had surged upward with gunpowder while Jan Zizka had occupied Sigismund's armies. In 1453 an invading army led by the Sultan Mohammed II laid siege to Constantinople. That "Rome of the East" had dimmed in grandeur since its defenders had broiled Arabs in Greek fire, but its massive walls stood intact, supposedly impregnable. The great fortifications were easily the ultimate of feudalism's defensive works.

The Turks, numbering eighty thousand, arrayed before Constantinople's walls a superlative of their own. It was the greatest artillery train yet to be assembled on earth. Fourteen batteries of cannon, totaling sixty-nine guns of all sizes, thrust their iron mouths toward the city's defenders, threatening fire, fumes, and balls of death.

Thirteen of the cannon were of gigantic size and could fire stone balls that weighed more than half a ton each. Two such balls measuring forty-six inches in diameter may be seen today in a Turkish museum at Istanbul.

One cannon, named Basilica, was a monster among monsters. Sixty oxen were required to drag it on sled runners. Two hundred men marched with the oxen to goad them onward. Another two hundred men went ahead with spades, picks, and axes to clear a roadway. The gunners, the elite, followed Basilica on Arabian horses draped in silks.

At sunrise, April 6, the sixty-nine cannon were ready for firing. The Sultan, gorgeously robed and astride a black charger, raised his jeweled hand. Hundreds of drums began beating, eighty thousand Turks began cheering, and the guns belched their lightning and thunder as one. Sixty-nine stones struck the city's walls, all aimed at one section in a concentrated fire.

It took two hours to load the larger gun-monsters. That meant that each big gun could be fired only seven times every fourteen hours. However, from dawn to dark the bombardment went on without pause, the smaller cannon filling the pauses with their own thuds of doom.

All through April, on into May, each sunrise was followed by the thumping of the drums, the invaders' wild cheers, and the answering crashes of the Turkish artillery. Each night shrouded a growing pile of stone rubble below one section of the city's walls.

By the end of May, the lowest Turk ox tender could see that it was only a matter of the Sultan's whim that Christendom's mightiest citadel had not become a

Turkish prize, one of the greatest ever won by arms. A ragged gap showed in the fortifications, a gap big enough to admit an army.

On Tuesday, May 29, 1453, the Turks poured through that gap amid drumming and cheering. That night Sultan Mohammed II sat on the throne of Constantine the Great while his victorious soldiers made merry in Constantinople's streets.

More than a city had fallen. With it fell a concept of government by sword and stone fort that had dominated Europe for most of a millennium.

Gunpowder had barely started to march!

Chapter 5

KINGS, GUNS, AND GOLD

DURING the three hundred and fifty years after the fall of Constantinople, gunpowder and guns cast the master mold of our age, call it the Machine Age, Atomic Age, or age of the Common Man as you will. The direction of the Americas' future was established two centuries before the Declaration of Independence led to the birth of the United States, and it was set in gun smoke.

Our school texts say little of the overwhelming influence upon today's world that was wielded by the black explosive Roger Bacon unleashed. However, the facts stand clear in history's record — one has but to sort them from the mass.

Military scholars describe Mohammed II of the victorious Ottoman Turks as the first great gunner of history. Long before him, we recall, the brown-skinned Arabs were familiar with gunpowder, and the Chinese were probably its inventors. We recall, too, that in Europe gunpowder was decried by the feudal lords who ruled.

All of this poses a huge question. In the hands of the Asiatics was an explosive weapon that was capable of giving them supremacy throughout the world for centuries to come. Why did they not push on to mastery?

Everything seemed weighted in their favor. The Asians had also developed the bow, and in the past had swept with it to peaks of military conquest. Witness the triumphs of Attila the Hun, and of the mighty Mongols Genghis Khan and Tamerlane. Witness as well the conquest of Spain by Moslem peoples of North Africa with the help of Negro troops. Now, Constantinople!

All that guarded the white man's Europe were the castles of warring barons, and walled cities whose defenses were puny compared to the great fortification that had failed to protect the "Rome of the East."

Compared with those developed in Asia, the crafts of Europe were crude. The finest silks and rugs and perfumes were Oriental. Lucky was the Christian knight who could boast that his sword was of Damascus steel, a product of Syrian and Persian artisans. For the newest in science, the highest in learning, Europe's scholars had to pore over Arabian manuscripts. The riches of India were the dream of Europe's kings.

Yet, looking back, we can see some odd gaps in the glowing record. The cannon of Mohammed II had *not* been forged by any ironmaster of the East. Cannon were clumsy, ugly things that held no appeal to craftsmen in the ancient arts passed on by father to son for countless generations. These men took pride in the fine edge of a Damascus blade or in the gold inlays of a sultan's suit of armor. So Mohammed had found no cannon foundries at home or among his Oriental neighbors. Instead, he had gone to a rough-and-ready Hungarian named Urban, of Europe's underground guns industry. Or perhaps it was Urban who sought the Sultan, order book in hand. In either event, Mohammed's great cannon were cast in Europe.

The very perfection to which the bow, the sword, and armor had been carried by the East's brown and yellow peoples caused their war lords to be even slower than the feudal barons in adopting explosive weapons. The Turks' use of big guns was a departure from the rule. Moreover, the Turks, themselves, were still firing stone cannon balls as late as 1807, a fact that sharply points the East's lack of zeal in mechanical progress.

The most astonishing delay of all in embracing gunpowder as a war weapon was China's. In 1860, or possibly a thousand years after the first pop of a Chinese-made firecracker, her soldiers were still using crossbows in battle.

Because of these things the course of civilization turned westward, to the Europe that in 1453 was still a raw frontier compared to Asia, civilization's birthplace.

Europe's crude gunpowder industry, banned and reviled but much alive, could not have asked for better advertising than was given it by the success of its cannon at Constantinople. Its smelly saltpeter sheds and primitive foundries were soon overwhelmed with orders, and fresh forges began to light the night with their glowing fires.

Kings were the chief patrons. A new king of France went after England's longbowmen with a siege train of hired cannon, won sixty battles in sixteen months, and ended Norman England's claim to power on the continent of Europe. It was a mighty turn of events.

Castle battering became a way to establish royal rule. The castles of lesser robber barons were blasted first and plundered. The plunder was used to hire greater cannon capable of reducing to rubble the largest baronial strongholds. The cities that had become independent states behind their high walls were bombarded into submission. Others were not long in coming to terms.

So kingdoms, nations under a central government, took form as feudalism's death sentence, written by Czech peasants and signed by a sultan, was carried out by royal rulers. Amid gunpowder's smoke modern Europe began to emerge.

Actually, this change was possible only because of the hired gunners, who were quite as willing to serve one king as another at a price.

The contract prices were high, and grew ever higher, which contributed hugely to the rise of kings to supreme power. They were the only ones with the wherewithal to pay. For the first time, the financing of a war became as important as waging it, and ended was the era when any local despot could maintain a private army.

Many factors, all new, brought about the rising costs. Gunpowder destroyed itself upon being fired. Cannon balls could rarely be shot again. This kind of waste was unknown with the old weapons. A sword, pike, or bow was usually good for battle after battle, and arrows could be fired over and over, the enemy's included. A bowman had but to pick up the arrow just shot at him and fire it back.

Moreover, cannon and firearms could not be made in home workshops by any farmhand in his spare time. Foundries and factories had to be built and workmen had to be trained in special skills. These investments were purposeless without further investments in powder mills.

The old weapons had been largely unchanged for hundreds of years. The new weapons were subject to a rapidly rising crescendo of changes, each of which added to the costs. And as kings began to war on kings, more and more cannon had to be placed under contract to meet the trend toward bigger and bigger wars.

A bare four decades after Constantinople's fall, only the most powerful of Europe's kings could afford the luxury of a major war. No longer could an army live wholly off a plundered countryside. It needed bases of supply for its gunpowder and shot. It needed roads over which supplies could pass and cannon could roll — they were now mounted on gun carriages and drawn by horses. All of this summed up to the most vital need: gold! Money was the newest war munition.

In 1492, Europe struck gold!

While seeking India, with its silks and spices, an Italian sailor in the hire of Spain discovered what

Europeans called the New World, and later the Americas. The silks and spices were lacking, but here was wealth enough of other kinds to make the most costly guns seem cheap to the king who tapped that wealth, as Spain promptly proceeded to do.

Why not! The natives of the New World had seen the lightning and heard the thunder of guns. The first white men were looked upon as gods, especially those in gleaming armor who rode horses.

We do not know how different the story might have been if Christopher Columbus and those following him had invaded the Americas on foot, armed only with swords, pikes, and bows. The American Indian was as good as any other man at sending an arrow to its mark, and ten million Indians, or more, inhabited the two continents. They were masters of fighting from cover, a type of warfare that was strange to Europeans long accustomed to fight in feudal ways. The Indians, moreover, knew every forest trail, every stream.

We do know what happened with gunpowder's help, plus that of the horse. Hernando Cortez and a few hundred Spaniards conquered the Aztecs of Mexico in less than two years. Another handful of Spanish adventurers led by Francisco Pizarro overthrew the Incas of Peru and, at a stroke, won most of South America.

The two feats were unparalleled. The forces of Cortez and Pizarro together totaled only about five hundred men, yet they won the major portion of the New World for the crown of Spain. Gold untold, wealth that awed, began flowing back to Spain by shiploads.

Most of it was spent for more gunpowder, more cannon, more power for this nation that itself had just broken from the grip of the Moors.

Spain became the dominant power in both the New and the Old Worlds. And a still mightier turn of history was pointed by her conquests of natives armed only with non-explosive weapons. During the next few centuries, gunpowder and guns made in Europe were to extend foreign supremacy over most of Africa, India, and other populated parts of the globe.

The system known as colonialism, by which dominion over vast areas became European, evolved directly from European superiority in producing and using explosives, first for conquest, next for police power, and finally for industrial development.

As Spain tightened her grip on Mexico, her gold hunters with guns fanned out into Florida, Texas, and the Pacific Southwest. Cortez gave California its name almost a century before the Pilgrim Fathers from England set foot on Plymouth Rock. By 1565, the West Indies were completely in Spanish hands, the settlement of Florida was begun at St. Augustine, and it seemed that the entire Western Hemisphere was going to become a colony of Spain, the Atlantic Ocean a Spanish lake.

So it seemed, and so easily North America could have been as Spanish in language and tradition as is most of South America today. But conflicting forces already were building up in England, where Henry VIII then ruled.

It is usual to think of Henry VIII, first, as the king who married six queens and rid himself of two by way of questionable divorces and two by lopping off their heads. He is well worth a second thought, for he did much to shape our era. Shrewd, utterly selfish, ruthless, his passion was for power, and in gunpowder he saw a new means to power that was missed completely by the rulers of Spain's growing empire.

Ships next enter our drama of kings, guns, and gold. Spain's control of the Atlantic, and thereby of the Americas' future, depended largely on the galleon, a ship of three or four decks that was at once a floating fort and a treasure ship. The galleon was armed with cannon, but mainly for defense. Primary reliance in attack was placed upon a ship's garrison of soldiers armed with swords, pikes, and a much improved handgun, the arquebus.

This new weapon, invented in 1521, was the predecessor of the musket. It was fired by a trigger that applied a match to a pan of powder. Though a blundering, unreliable weapon by later standards, it was then such an improvement that Spain favored it above cannon. The galleon's tactics were to get within close range of an enemy ship, subdue her defenders by arquebus fire, then grapple and pour soldiers aboard to fight hand to hand. Capture of the enemy ship was the goal.

Such tactics were as antique as galleys rowed by slaves and bearing soldiers armed with battle-axes. The

Spaniards simply had fitted out these ancient practices with new trimmings.

Not so with Henry VIII. Whatever were his faults, one was not backward vision. He was the first king to see that a warship armed with cannon could shell an enemy ship from long range, and then blast it from the sea by a broadside of gunfire. Capture of the enemy was his last thought. He sought to destroy with a minimum of risk to his own ships. Henry developed the broadside cannon attack and used ships crowded with sail that could hit and run. The fact that this kind of warfare was considered ignoble at the time did not bother Henry at all. He was the herald of modern war fought at long range.

Of course such ships were expensive, and Henry had no stream of gold from America. But he did have a wife, his first, who had failed to bear him a son and for that reason was unwanted. The wife, Catherine of Aragon — it is historic irony that she was of Spanish blood — proved indirectly to hold the key to hoards of treasure right in England.

When in 1533 Henry divorced her, and the Pope refused to approve the divorce, Henry renounced the Roman Catholic Church, then England's only church. The new Church of England was established, and Henry became its head. Promptly, as a side issue of the divorce controversy with the Pope, he seized all of the Catholic monasteries in his realm, together with the wealth they had amassed under feudalism. About one fifth of the whole land and its revenues came under control of the crown.

Gold from the monasteries now built Henry's new cannon-powered fleet, the first modern navy. By 1547, upon his death, the fleet numbered fifty-three ships armed with 2085 guns. That was not all Henry left England. Shipbuilding had become a permanent industry. Foundries for casting cannon formed the core of a second infant industry in iron and brass. Gunpowder mills, using improved methods, were refashioning the old alchemists into chemists.

The basic concept of war was changed. Of old, the bow and sword and pike, the weapon in hand, had served the fighting man. That order was now reversed. Weapons counted above warriors! Men served the guns, not guns the men, and so did all else aboard England's new ships. The warship was evolving into a fighting machine with lines of supply that reached all the way back to the ore mines. Soon the *munitions* of war became more vital to victory than either soldiers or sailors!

On the warships, skills in seamanship, gunnery, and the handling of gunpowder took precedence over fighting courage — brains outranked brawn. The master of a battery was worth far more than any old-style hero capable only of bashing enemy heads.

All signs in that navy of the foggy past indicated the trend that, four centuries later, was to make the scientist armed with isotopes and atoms the most feared, the ultimate among warriors!

The next act rounds out the most crucial of all the sequences in the drama of Henry VIII. The real test of the soundness of his naval policy did not come until 1588, a full generation after his death. Then England faced the Invincible Armada of Spain, and the new tactics based on the use of gunpowder were opposed by the whole weight of war's entrenched past. That test was to determine the future of England as well as of North America and much of the world. It was left to the decision of a woman.

Enter England's great queen, Elizabeth I.

She was the daughter of Henry and Anne Boleyn, the wife for whom Henry had cast aside Catherine, renounced the Pope, and had dared to defy the wrath of Spain. These extreme steps had been prompted by the hope of a son from Anne. How bitterly Henry was disappointed by the birth of a girl is indicated by the consequences. Anne Boleyn was beheaded. Her marriage to Henry was declared illegal, the child Elizabeth illegitimate.

The events that in 1558 made her queen when she was twenty-five need not concern us. It is enough to grasp the improbable plot that mounted to a crisis during her middle age. One unwanted woman, Catherine, had unwittingly opened the door to the church gold and made possible the navy by which, in right hands, Henry might win historic acclaim, and he valued acclaim second only to power. Time had passed, and now another woman, the child of a beheaded wife, held the navy's fate in her hands.

Make no mistake: The decision was solely Elizabeth's. The day when the navy would be the nation's and supported by the taxes of its people was yet to arrive. As a holdover of feudalism, the ships built by Henry were Elizabeth's as much as were the shoes that she wore. She could keep or discard the ships as readily as the shoes.

The Navy's Lord High Admiral was her employee, paid from her personal income, as were all officers, men, suppliers, builders. She could rent or sell her ships or do away with all of them without asking anybody's permission. It was her private navy. Its duty was to the crown, which was a form of royal insurance for continued power.

In the event of war, the queen was expected to devote her navy to the country's defense, just as owners of merchant ships were on call. Then and only then could she ask the people, through Parliament, for taxes to help defray the navy's extra war costs. The nearest thing similar to modern taxes that the queen could levy were duties upon goods imported from other countries. Aside, we might note that England had no national debt, and that the cost of government to the people was nil — it was borne by the ruler as the price of the privilege of ruling.

Unlike Henry VIII, Elizabeth had no church gold to squander, and the income from royal lands had been sadly reduced by the bungling of a king and a queen who had preceded her. She was pinched for money, often in debt and forced to borrow from money lenders.

The fleet that she inherited was not Henry's proud fleet, but one wasted by neglect and dishonesty. Many ships were unseaworthy from lack of repair, the crews were unpaid, their pay in captains' pockets.

England had plenty of old seafighters who held gunpowder in low regard. They were glad to watch Henry's ships rot, having liked neither him nor his tactics, which, they felt, were a coward's way to fight. But close to Elizabeth, too, were sea dogs of a new breed, men who had sailed the Spanish Main and raided many a treasure ship: Sir Francis Drake, Sir John Hawkins, Sir Walter Raleigh, Martin Frobisher. These names were to ring through history in tales of bold ventures, and to be immortalized in the future names of faraway bays and towns. Their advice was that gunpowder, cannon, and clouds of sail would dictate the security of England.

Elizabeth never married. As her hair grayed and she dyed it to the fair auburn of her youth, she liked to say that she had married England. More than anything else, the woman who had been the unwanted girl sought to be popular. She had no cause to honor either her father or his works, but if his tactics would save men and ships, as Drake assured her they would, that was reason to adopt them, though it meant sacrifice.

To raise money to restore the fleet, Elizabeth imposed economies at court. She sold some of the royal lands. In 1577, Hawkins was made the Navy's treasurer with full authority to end corruption and see that the money was honestly spent. A mill that would assure a plentiful supply of gunpowder was built at Waltham Abbey.

In all this work Drake was not only the consultant, but also a procurer of funds. Secretly in partnership with the queen, he sailed on a freebooting voyage to the West Indies, to return with a shipload of Spanish gold. It helped build English ships.

The first test of the new ships was in 1587. By then Spain was in the midst of mustering, at the port of Cadiz on her Atlantic coast, the largest war fleet ever assembled until then. The Spanish king, Philip II, bothered by gout and a cataract in one eye, had decided to put an end to English raids on his gold ships, and at the same time to return Elizabeth's petty kingdom to the Catholic Church. Petty, indeed, England seemed: she had but three million people to Spain's eight million.

One April dawn, while the forts that guarded the harbor still slept and the sun was just tipping the forest of Spanish masts, a broadside of cannon awoke Cadiz to an unprecedented sight. The gun smoke cleared to disclose Drake's ship, the *Golden Hind,* canvas spread, bearing down upon the nearest of the clumsy galleons riding at anchor. A second broadside ripped into the galleon's timbered hulk, she began to sink, and the *Golden Hind* swung her guns toward the next anchored victim.

In Drake's wake followed an English squadron of the new men-o'-war, sails billowing, batteries blazing. The invaders came like sea hawks out of the dawn —

by comparison, the Spanish galleons were fat pelicans. Salvos of broadsides tore into the Spanish ships. Havoc spread everywhere in the Bay of Cadiz, and then the raiding ships vanished in the fog of their own powder smoke as quietly as they had appeared.

Here was an epochal advance in naval warfare, a logical coupling of explosive power with speed in attack and escape. Thousands of tons of Spanish shipping were destroyed or damaged at a cost, to Drake's squadron, of only a few bullet holes in the sails.

"El Draque," the Dragon, the Spaniards called the bold raider who, as he put it, had singed the King of Spain's beard. Thereafter Philip spoke of Elizabeth as a she-devil. His venture against her became a crusade.

A year was spent in repairing Drake's damage and rounding up more ships. This time, Philip resolved, his fleet would be unbeatable, an invincible Armada. Applying Drake's lesson, the king added more cannon but disdained to train gunners and sailors in Drake's methods. His reliance remained in soldiers and handguns, and in the ancient boarding tactics.

The Armada got under sail early in 1588. It numbered 132 ships of all kinds, and carried 21,621 soldiers and 8066 sailors. So tightly were the soldiers jammed aboard that one might suppose every man stood on another's toes and slept upright. Decks were soon awash as the overloaded vessels wallowed in squally seas. Seasickness added to the misery of the soldiers, few of whom had ever been to sea before.

How tightly they were packed into the holds may be

judged by a modern comparison. The combined tonnage of the 132 Spanish ships was 59,190 tons, then a huge total. The largest ocean liner used as a troopcarrier in World War II, which happened to be England's *Queen Elizabeth,* weighed 83,673 tons, or a fourth more than the whole Armada. The big liner carried only 12,000 troops on any one trip, even during the war's worst extremities.

Rough seas, wrecks, and other troubles forced the Armada to put into Lisbon, Portugal, for a fresh overhauling. Not until late in July did a lookout on England's south coast sight the oncoming invasion fleet heading toward the port of Plymouth.

Elizabeth's Lord High Admiral was Lord Howard of Effingham. Drake, Hawkins, and Frobisher were among his fighting commanders. The queen's Navy numbered fewer than forty warships and probably a hundred and fifty other vessels of the merchant trades. Every English ship capable of carrying a gun had been pressed into service.

The English warships also had soldiers aboard, as a concession to stubborn champions of the old fighting practices. But for every soldier there were three sailors — an almost exact reversal of the Spanish strategy. The sailors, moreover, were highly trained and knew English waters. They included about eight hundred seamen who were schooled in long-range gunnery.

The sailors and gunners were quickly directing the tactics of the battle. Spain's army, ready with pikes and grappling irons for boarding, never had a chance to fight.

As the great Armada stood off Plymouth for battle, the tactics of Drake at Cadiz, of sea hawks against pelicans, were repeated on a larger scale. The English were ever on the move, never quite within range of the Spanish handguns, while balls from the big English guns screamed toward the Spaniards, seemingly from nowhere. Lord Howard reported later, "There was never seen a more terrible value of great shot."

The Spanish ships still afloat fled to Calais on the French side of the English Channel. The English sent blazing tar-soaked ships into the anchored Armada, forcing it in panic back into the open sea to escape being destroyed by fire.

Facing the English once more, again tormented by the cannon, the Spanish High Admiral decided to run rather than fight. The only way of escape was north, into the North Sea and thence around the rugged north coast of Scotland. Even the English knew little of these waters, and the Spanish knew nothing of them.

The North Sea summer is generally calm, but not that summer of 1588. High winds and storms lashed the fleeing ships of Spain, and wrecks added to the already high damage and loss from gunfire. Rations ran short, scurvy and fever invaded the crowded holds.

Throughout the battle England lost not a ship. Probably less than half of Philip's fleet, mighty by the old standards of war, returned to Spain. The other half perished somewhere along the way.

So perished, too, the possibility that North America would become Spanish in language and tradition. So began Great Britain's rule of the seas, to continue for the next 350 years.

Chapter 6

READY! AIM! FIRE!

Wᴇ have seen how gunpowder and guns raised Czech peasants to the role of conquerors. We have seen, under Henry VIII, how the advancing explosive changed naval warfare, fostered new skills among seamen and landsmen alike, and began the expansion of English industry.

Changes just as sweeping were brought about by powder and guns in Europe's armies, her roads, bridges, canals, and manufactured products, and above all in the lot of the common man, as we shall see next.

With the rising strength of central governments in Europe, the dependence of kings upon the free companies of soldiers grew less and less. The kings began to organize professional armies of their own, each a permanent national force. The recruiting, training, clothing, feeding, and equipping of the armies with explosive weapons, the transportation of troops in emergency, the maintaining of their morale and loyalty, posed problems that, in the solving, were to alter much of the life of Europe.

None of the new armies was so grandly organized, none was so to influence the future, as that of Louis XIV of France, so it shall be our example. Louis reveled in being known as the Sun King and *Le Grand Monarque*. His reign from 1643 to 1715 was the longest, his court the most magnificent in Europe's history. His own summing up of his power, "I am the state!" was not far wrong, for back of it was a masterly new adaptation of the power of gunpowder to statecraft.

Europe could hardly believe what it saw happen: The glitter of Louis' court was extended to the French soldier of the humblest origin. Peasants that had been of too low an order for feudal lords to count among war's dead were put into polished boots, belts, and uniforms. Peasants became the king's right arm.

Henry VIII of England had uniformed some of his troops and is credited with introducing uniforms to modern warfare. Before him, uniforms had been limited to liveries provided by a few great nobles to their immediate servants. The nearest that an entire army had come to uniforms by the mid-sixteen hundreds was the wearing of distinctive armbands, or cloth patches, an innovation of King Gustavus Adolphus of Sweden.

Louis XIV put into uniform, complete to the last shoelace, an army that, at its peak, numbered 385,000 officers and men. This was his personal army, supported by the royal treasury, just as was England's royal fleet.

The uniforms were neither an extravagance nor a benevolence. They identified the soldier as being a king's man and therefore inspired his pride, fortified his morale. They marked friends from enemies in battle. The success of campaigns was no longer dependent upon armored knights, but upon foot soldiers with guns. Moreover, the uniform made the recruiting task in Louis' France infinitely easier. Never before had mere peasants been offered such grandeur, and of the entire French Army, 330,000 were infantry armed with muskets and bayonets.

The musket was an improved arquebus. Bear hunters of the Pyrenees, the rugged mountains between France and Spain, had improvised the first bayonets by fitting hunting knives into their gun barrels for defense against bears that were not killed by the first shot. In due course, the bayonet was developed, taking its name from the French city of Bayonne. It doomed the sword and pike, as guns had doomed the bow, and made the infantryman two fighting men in one.

Some ten thousand of Louis' infantry were mounted on horses and given the proud name of dragoons. Men whose grandfathers had been serfs now rode to war just as knights or dukes, their officers, did.

The lowest private of the least-extolled regiment bloomed forth in a cocked hat trimmed with red piping, a knee-length coat of blue or gray, and red breeches tucked in red leggings. His buttons and buckles were brass. Sergeants wore red cuffs and pocket flaps, and as the scale of rank ascended, the profusion of color and braid, which became silver and gold, increased. The sleeves of officers were cuffed with lace, their headpieces adorned with furs and plumes. A model regiment, the King's Own, was uniformed to a man in white and gold.

Louis and his ministers did not stop with dress. Permanent masonry barracks were built for the troops, each with its courtyard for drills, parades, and military ceremonies. Instead of being routed from their bunks by the kick of a boot, these new soldiers of the king awoke to the call of bugles playing reveille, followed by music of the regimental band, another innovation.

The men were paid regularly. A quartermaster corps was organized to see that the usual fare of salt pork and biscuits was varied with fresh meat, vegetables, and fruit if possible. To assure the army its supplies wherever it moved, supply depots were built at important points around the nation. Roads, little better than trails, were transformed into the first system of national highways to be undertaken since the fall of ancient Rome. Streams were bridged, canals built.

At Essonne, near Paris, Louis built his own gunpowder plant. He preferred, like Elizabeth of England, to secure the main supply of powder in his own hands.

An Inspector General was appointed for the Army. He assigned inspectors to foundries, mills, and factories holding Army contracts to make sure that the goods were of the specified quality and delivered on time — a sign of the changing order indeed, for cheating the customer had long been a routine practice among suppliers.

Under these new pressures, manufacturers instituted changes of their own. Supplying so large an army with boots, belts, coats, trousers, leggings, and what not, to say nothing of guns, bayonets, and ammunition, demanded improved methods. For the first time, better management and sounder financing became common business terms, and industry underwent changes almost as extensive as those of the Army. Louis may not have been the originator of modern mass production, but the seeds from which it evolved were sown when he ordered uniforms and pieces of equipment by the tens of thousands.

Discipline was introduced into the Army and enforced with an iron hand. Every soldier was made to fit into a mold as unvarying as the uniform he wore. Rules covered every detail of conduct and appearance, and so began what today's American soldier knows as "spit and polish."

The rules were deliberately designed to set the soldier apart from the civilian, to create a military caste that lived in a world of its own. The Army established its own courts-martial, which are still with us. It did its best to end long centuries of officially encouraged soldier outrages against civilians perpetrated under the old feudal slogan of "go to war and loot as you will."

The plain soldier had rarely been noticed, let alone honored. Louis borrowed another idea, this time from England's Elizabeth. She had presented medals to heroes in the battle against the Armada. Louis had the best artists of France design medals, ribbons, and unit decorations that his generals might award at will for unusual valor or service, regardless of rank or birth. The presentation of awards was made an inspiring ceremony, and the hero received a kiss on each cheek.

A far-reaching change was made in the lot of the soldier who had been disabled in duty or was too old for further military service. For centuries on end, these victims of warfare had no recourse except to steal or beg. Louis founded the *Hotel des Invalides,* a home and hospital to care for the needy soldiers of France for the rest of their lives. It was the forerunner of veterans' benefits that today, the world around, have become a major responsibility of civilized governments.

Tactically, the army that *Le Grand Monarque* put into the field was also unlike any other of history. The best of the feudal armies had been little more than organized hordes. Battles had usually been decided by hand-to-hand combat. Now, with guns, war had become an issue of army against army, not men against men. The day of line formations had arrived.

Companies were formed into three ranks and faced the enemy in company fronts, each rank as straight as a ruler. Every soldier's elbows touched those of his comrades on either side, every musket was carried exactly as every other, and all muskets were loaded and fired in perfect unison upon command. Men were so rigidly trained that they marched toward possible death with the iron will of robots. They were merely parts of a single fighting machine, the company.

In turn, each company was a unit of a larger machine, the regiment. Each regiment was a part of the brigade, the brigade of the division, the division of the corps, the corps of the Army.

As with England's new style Navy, the new style

Army was steadily becoming more and more dependent upon the daily work and morale of civilians on
farms, in shops, factories, and banks, and, above all,
on the inventor who might alter the best plans of generals overnight. A failure in a vital point of supply,
such as ammunition, could mean loss of a war. This
developing pattern was to have tremendous consequences in the centuries ahead. The plow, the loom,
the mill, the foundry, the mine, the road, the bridge
had become war weapons just as much as were gunpowder and guns.

No display of armored knights charging into battle
surpassed the martial splendor of Louis' Army march-
ing into action. The precisely aligned battalions, rank
on rank, extended as far as the eye could see, a dazzle
of color, glinting bayonets, and regimental standards.
Bugles rang out commands, drums beat, regimental
bands played, and rigid uniformed lines went forward,
every soldier in step with the music.

Then the bugles would blare more shrilly, the music
and drums would fade into silence, and all along the
advancing front the voices of officers would cry "Halt!"
The butts of thousands of muskets would clap the
ground in a jarring thud. Again the bugles and the
captains' commands would rise in crescendo:

"Ready-y!"

"Aim-m-m!"

"fire!"

The muskets would blaze as one from the far right
flank of the front to the far left flank, and the gun

smoke of the massive volley would float away in white clouds. To the infantry of France had come the broad-side of the English warship. Muskets were now echoing cannon.

As the enemy replied in kind, gaps appeared in the line. Then ranks would close until every elbow again touched elbow. The only pause would be to reload. Then, once more, the bugles would blare and the drums would roll in cadence to the captains' cries of "Forwa-a-ard, march!"

And something as new as pensions happened once the boots had marched on. Stretcher-bearers searched out wounded men and bore them to medical aid sta-tions on the field. Doctors and surgeons took over their care. Later, ambulances removed the wounded to hos-pitals. The foot soldier was a man who had been trained at no small effort and cost. He must be saved to fight another day. He now represented an investment.

In time, these reforms expanded to the armies of every civilized nation. Those changes of humane turn, such as care of the disabled and old, were adopted for civilian workers by forward-looking industries and governments, until today pensions and other benefits are looked upon as routine rights by uncounted mil-lions of plain people.

If, however, you are thinking that Louis deserves credit for compassion and that his concern for the common soldier was prompted by his heart, erase the thought. His reforms were prompted solely by expedi-ency, by hard business need, which in turn was fostered by the steady advances being made in guns and gunpowder and the changes they forced on the character of war itself.

The advances in weapons were well under way when Louis took the throne. The flintlock musket was replacing the matchlock or arquebus, and it was a more reliable weapon. The hammer struck a spark from flint into a covered powder pan, which kept the powder from being lost and helped to protect it from the rain. The flintlock was light enough to be aimed and fired from the shoulder, whereas the clumsy matchlock had been aimed and fired from the chest.

Next, paper cartridges were invented. No longer did the soldier have to measure out each load of loose powder and carry packets of wads and bullets. The ready-made cartridges doubled the rate of fire. By 1700 the trained infantryman could fire two rounds a minute.

Gunpowder was much improved. It was of a higher degree of purity, better mixed, cleaner burning, though a cannon still had to be swabbed out after every firing and gunners' faces were soon smoke-blackened. Moreover, powder grains came now in seven sizes, from finely ground grains used in handguns only, to pellets as big as walnuts for the largest cannon. The size increased with the size of the weapon and the shot.

At the cost of an unrecorded number of lives, burst cannon, and disasters in early powder mills, men had learned that the size of the powder grains regulated their speed of combustion, and that coarsely grained, and therefore slower-burning, powders were needed in firing the heavy iron balls used in cannon. The retarded rate of burning allowed the explosive energy a split second in which to exert itself against the ball, instead of suddenly bursting its full force against the gun chamber. That discovery had made it possible to increase the range of cannon to one or two miles.

Powder mills, too, were vastly improved. The mixing and pressing of the raw materials into powder cakes, and the granulating or "corning" of the powder into pellets, was no longer done wholly by hand. Methods used in grinding olives and pressing oil from the pulp mechanically, by means of wooden stamps or wheels operated by windmills or water power, had been adapted to powder manufacture, again after a frightful toll of lives. The dank quarters in which alchemists had made gunpowder, and the later sheds and cellars that had supplied powder to the free companies, were now soldier-guarded stone establishments over which, as at Essonne near Paris and at Waltham Abbey in England, floated the royal flag.

The odorous saltpeter sheds were passing into history in every nation of Europe except the most backward. The reason for their passing was the discovery in India of huge natural deposits of saltpeter, which had somehow accumulated there in the far past. The Indian saltpeter beds, which then seemed inexhaustible, plus manufacturing methods borrowed from the ancient olive oil industry, made possible the production of gunpowder in Europe on a large scale.

These changes, and others less consequential, all added up to a new factor in war: mass fire power capable of killing or wounding wholesale at a distance of as much as a mile or more. Hand-to-hand fighting on land, except in extremes, was now as obsolete as boarding by grappling irons had become in naval warfare. The chief object on land, as at sea, was to outshoot the enemy, to riddle him with a hail of lead before coming to grips. The infantry broadside, which was concentrated fire power, had become the ultimate of fighting power.

The broadside served another end: it prevented some of the waste of gunpowder which always occurs in battle when men fire at will. And gunpowder costs per pound were about five times what they are today.

Generally, costs were a factor in promoting most, if not all, of the reforms made in the soldier's behalf. Five years of effort and money were required to train an infantryman to the extreme degree of discipline that the new tactics demanded, to make him forget his own instincts and fears in battle, and to obey commands automatically. Once any soldier had been so trained, it became only good sense and sound economy to do everything possible to keep him in the Army and in good physical condition.

Men do not like to die, however gloriously, nor do they like to be turned into robots. Confronted by these truths, the military planners set out to make army life as appealing as possible to French youth. Serfdom had been broken, and no new form of compulsory military

service had as yet come into effect. That meant Louis'
Army, as originally conceived, was dependent on
volunteers.

Therefore there evolved the glamour of the uniform,
the medals and the ribbons, the bugles and the bands;
the regular pay, barracks, better food, care of those who
were disabled or grew old in the service of their king.
No other career then offered the youth of France such
inducements.

Lastly, an appeal was made to Frenchmen as Frenchmen, as loyal subjects of *Le Grand Monarque.* To die
if need be in his service and for France was held to be
the most glorious way a Frenchman could die. Patri-
otism became a new weapon in the grand Army's
arsenal, and so did propaganda.

As history reckons time, the collapse of feudalism
was still too recent for the ordinary person, not only
in France but also throughout the rest of Europe, to
grasp the fact that the old baronial fiefs were now
united under a supreme monarch. The deposed barons
were not eager to accept the change forced upon them
by cannon, nor was the clergy either, which also had
fallen from its former influence.

The result was that loyalties were still local, not
national. The peasant, who made up the bulk of the
population, was concerned mainly with his own little
farm and village, and still took off his hat and bowed
to the local lord. Paris was a long way off. Popular
pride in France, as a nation, was yet to be awakened.

Into this lethargy Louis hurled a bolt of self-advertising so grandly dazzling that no Frenchman could help hearing about it, for soon all Europe was talking about the new wonder. At Versailles, near Paris, he built the most magnificent palace ever devised for a king of the west. You ask, what has a palace to do with explosives? The answer is that no such palace as Versailles could have been built if gunpowder and guns had not changed completely the character of war.

Artisans and laborers from all over France shared in the building, which made the project a form of royal largess. Artists and sculptors were commissioned to embellish not only the enormous main palace, with its great Hall of Mirrors, but also what became a whole community of lesser palaces and buildings. The work went on for years, years that steadily proclaimed the grandeur and generous hand of King Louis XIV.

Naturally, men made comparisons. And compared with this new royal center, the grim castles of the greatest of the old feudal barons, castles now mostly in ruins, appeared as crude and primitive as cavemen's haunts. Here was an object lesson that every mind could grasp.

The climactic glory of Versailles was in its gardens. Their vast lawns and beds of blooms and aisles of trees of every kind, the gorgeous fountains and pools and statuary, were of a variety and beauty that left visitors breathless. The gardens alone, cleared out of a forest, cost an estimated hundred million dollars. The exact cost will never be known, for Louis destroyed all bills.

And nowhere in the spacious sweep of Versailles was

there a defensive wall or moat or battlement, such as the lords of old had found necessary to secure their power in the day of sword, pike, and bow. Louis' seat of government was as open as a public park. That freedom from defensive works was the salient message dramatized by Versailles. The message was that the king's security reposed in the men of France, in the royal Army deployed along the frontiers of the nation, a hundred, three hundred miles distant. In a word, gunpowder guaranteed Versailles' safety.

At intervals a great public show was staged there. Early in the evening, as the crowds gathered, the batteries of fountains would play in all the colors of the rainbow. Music would drift over the gardens from a resplendently uniformed Army band. Then, when complete darkness had fallen, a rocket would loft itself skyward and scatter a thousand stars. Blaze after blaze of rockets would follow, fiery pinwheels spinning and showering sparks, and fireworks of all kinds in unbelievable profusion would take command of the night, hissing, exploding in brilliant bursts. The night air would be pungent with the odor of gunpowder. The odor even permeated the perfumed bedchamber of the king.

Throughout Europe, other kings copied *Le Grand Monarque* as best they could, in advertising the supremacy of royal rule. Many other palaces of open gardens were built. French became the language of most European courts. Royal anthems were written.

And when a king appeared at any of his Army posts on occasions of ceremony, the very ground was made to tremble by the thunder of cannon fired in royal salute. Or did the cannon thunder in warning of something that even the great Louis overlooked: that gunpowder had made all men tall?

For a time Louis' reforms did bring soldiers into his grand Army as volunteers. The old type of mercenary adventurers — Swiss, Germans, Swedes, Scots, Irish, Russians, for hire by anybody — were weeded from the ranks of most regiments. The Army became French more completely than any army before it, a truly national Army.

But it still remained the Army of the king, subject to his whim. It was not the Army of the people of France. Mutterings of discontent began to be heard, the whispers of rebellion. Constant wars, supposedly in the public interest, led to heavy taxation as Louis shifted the burden of cost upon the people.

Louis might have heeded an omen in England. By 1688, just a century after defeat of Spain's Armada, the royal Navy was almost twice the old tonnage of the Armada and totaled 173 ships and nearly 7000 cannon. Acting on behalf of England's people, Parliament decided that a navy of such size was too great to be entrusted to any man's whim, even a king's. The English Navy became royal only in name, the Navy of all Britain! The people took over not only its support, through taxes levied by Parliament, but also an Admiralty controlled by Parliament took over the Navy's direction. It became the people's Navy.

Louis also ignored reforms in his grand Army that were as badly needed as those he had already made. Regiments were the properties of their colonels, and could be bought and sold like any other property. The colonels, in effect, were businessmen who contracted with the king to enlist men and manage the regimental units for a fee. The system was rotten with dishonesty and all sorts of abuses.

Under no condition could an enlisted man hope to become an officer. All commissions were limited strictly to aristocrats, to the sons of noble families. The man in the ranks, however glorified by medals and uniforms and a glittering king's new attentions, had to remain in the ranks as a penalty of his birth.

Propaganda is two-edged: promote a man's esteem in himself and his career, and you also promote his ambition to better his lot. War, too, is a great leveler of men, a great exposer of veneers and false values.

The mutterings in the ranks became a rumble; the stream of French youth volunteering for the Army dwindled to a trickle, then stopped. In theory, the volunteer system continued; actually it became a travesty. To keep their regiments filled with "volunteers," the colonel-contractors resorted to blackmail, threats, suspended punishments, every type of coercion. Petty criminals were given a choice of Army service or jail. Many chose jail. Army desertions increased.

These corruptions, as well as huge debts, were passed on, in 1715, by Louis XIV to his successor, Louis XV, the king of the foreboding words, "After us the deluge." He, in turn, passed them on to Louis XVI, weak and dull, in a period that was most critical for all crowned heads. It was now 1774.

A new people, the North Americans, had entered the world scene. Their nation was founded on the premise that every man deserved the same opportunity as every other to better his lot, irrespective of low or high birth.

On July 4, 1776, the American people announced that they were no longer colonists of the English king, but a free and independent nation. Rebellions against kings were not new, but radically new was the Americans' creed expressed in their Declaration of Independence:

> We hold these truths to be self-evident, that all men are created equal, that they are endowed by their Creator with certain inalienable Rights, that among these are Life, Liberty, and the pursuit of Happiness.

We all know what was the outcome of that declaration in the United States of America. Less well-known is its effect on France. On the heels of American victory came the French Revolution, and from it a decree that was to be as far-reaching in influencing men's lives as was the Declaration of Independence.

The date, August 23, 1793, is one of the most memorable in our story of explosives, and of their reshaping of the affairs of mankind, for on that date the French Committee of Public Safety announced the first universal conscription for war:

> The young men shall fight; the married men shall forge weapons and transport supplies; the women will make tents and serve in the hospitals; the children will make up old linen into lint; the old men will have themselves carried into the public squares to rouse the courage of the fighting men, and to preach hatred of kings and the unity of the Republic. The public buildings shall be turned into barracks, the public squares into munition factories; the earthen floors of cellars will be treated with lye to extract saltpeter. All suitable firearms shall be turned over to the troops; the interior shall be policed with fowling pieces and with cold steel. All saddle horses shall be seized for the cavalry; all draft horses not employed in cultivation will draw the artillery and supply wagons.

Destiny's wheel had turned completely. The people, the rabble of the age before gunpowder, now seized the power first wielded by feudal lords and then by kings.

The trials of the first French Republic, from which rose Napoleon, and in due course Waterloo, are not part of our story except to note three major facts of lasting influence:

Napoleon, the first great modern dictator, rose from obscurity.

Most of his ablest generals rose from the ranks; they were men of the people.

The revolutionary proclamation of compulsory military service by every person able to serve created the nation in arms, and, for better or worse, or a measure of both, the nation in arms had come to stay — at least until the present day.

The United States is now a nation in arms.

Chapter 7

MARCH OF THE INVENTORS

MORE and more as we proceed, in our history of gunpowder, we shall notice something new making its appearance in the world: a growing freedom of opportunity. Its growth is almost in exact ratio with the receding powers of nobles and kings.

Every new invention usually develops the need of another invention, then of another, and another, until the consequence is an avalanche of progress. So, as we have seen, gunpowder led to cannon, and cannon to foundries in which guns could be cast. And the foundries demanded iron, more iron and better iron, coal and more coal for their blast furnaces.

France built its first blast furnace about 1550, and by 1600 thirteen foundries were at work, all devoted to manufacturing cannon. Scythes were about the only other product that they made. In Sweden, Russia, Hungary, and elsewhere arms factories also led to establishing the iron industry. A single Russian arms plant employed 683 workers as early as 1700. Only a few mills of any kind in Europe matched that size.

The demand for more iron raised the problem of how to mine it by more efficient methods. Fire setting, the ancient process, was much too slow and costly. According to this old method, a wood fire was built against the face of ore-bearing rock and kept burning day and night until the rock was heated through. Sometimes water was dashed on the hot rock to cause it to crack, but more often it was left to cool in the air and split during the cooling. Chunks of ore were then pried loose with a pick or a wedge, and broken up by hand with hammers and sledges.

For countless thousands of years, fire setting had filled all the needs for iron, and no reason existed to find any better method for mining it. But with cannon makers crying for iron, and musket makers for copper and lead as well, and the foundries for coal, mining was confronted by an urgent demand for improvement.

Gunpowder could not easily be overlooked in this search for a new mining tool. It was powerful enough to burst a cannon; why not rock? Besides, military engineers already had put it to use in splitting the walls of several feudal cities by tunneling underneath and exploding kegs of powder. In 1627 a Hungarian engineer, Kaspar Weindl, dared to experiment with gunpowder in ore mining.

Dared is the proper word. Up to now the explosive had been employed only to maim, kill, and destroy. Blowing up a city wall was not the same thing as breaking up rock in a mine. Ore had to be left undamaged by the explosion.

The mines in which Weindl did his pioneering were in a deep ravine of the Hungarian Ore Mountains, at the door of an ancient feudal town that bore the formidable name of Selmeczbánya. Worked since the eighth century, these mines yielded not only copper and lead, but also silver and gold. To make the risk of failure doubly grave, they were owned by the emperor. Any serious damage might cost Weindl his head.

He took that risk. Without boring tools to drill holes in the rock in which to put his powder, with only the haziest idea of what the force of his blast would do to the underground rock roof in the mine chamber, he packed powder deep into a crack, tamped and wadded it until it was tightly confined, laid a long fuse, and fired it. As the fuse sizzled, Weindl dashed for a safe spot.

The whole town, built in terraces on the mountainside, heard the dull thud of the explosion. When at length Weindl emerged from the mine's mouth, his broad smile indicated that his name was to be immortalized in the history of the explosives industry. In a split second his blast had loosed more ore-rich rock than fire setting and hand tools could produce in many days.

Kaspar Weindl was careful to record his feat. His notes are the first undisputed proof that a blast of gunpowder was good for something other than destruction.

Other mining engineers were most cautious about utilizing this discovery. They feared the effects of repeated blasts in underground workings. The lack of boring tools was another deterrent. Labor was cheap, gunpowder expensive. Here were new problems to be met by men making studies of rock strata, by tool inventors, by the makers of gunpowder who worked to reduce its costs and better fit it to the new task.

In Germany and in Sweden, however, daring followers of Weindl slowly improved on his knowledge and technique. The required rock drills which were cutting bars of tempered iron, replaced ancient picks and wedges. Powder costs were reduced. By 1670 an English traveler, Edward Brown, was astonished to find gunpowder used in most of Europe's larger mines.

In 1696 the Swiss essayed a second bold advance. Their little nation high in the Alps had more rock barriers to travel than armies of laborers could remove in centuries by the methods of road building. As in mining, fire setting was the one known way of removing rock above ground — or was it? The answer was a gunpowder blast that echoed and re-echoed through the Alps from lofty Albula Pass to snow-capped Mont Blanc. Over the months, other blasts followed, and what from time immemorial had been no more than a path became the Albula Road, a main thoroughfare for wagon travel.

Note the links in our lengthening chain. The push for iron had now started revolutions both in mining and road building. A third spread to quarrying stone for building construction. A fourth was to recast the future of the civilized world.

Two years after the Albula blasts, gunpowder's broadening influence prompted the invention of the first commercially useful steam-powered engine!

Probably the first man to tinker with a steam engine was a Greek inventor, Hero of Alexandria, who lived at about the time of Christ. He invented a steam-powered device for which no better use could be found than blowing organ pipes and turning spits before a fire in roasting meat. After all, no pressing need for steam power existed, and a good fifteen hundred years elapsed before it did.

Then the interest in mining that had been started by gunpowder brought the need for more power to the forefront. The deeper men went into the earth for iron and other metals, the more bothersome became the problem of water seepage into mine workings. Unless a way could be devised to pump out the water, and keep it pumped out, there would be less iron, less coal, perhaps the loss of many mines.

All over Europe engineers took up the problem. In France several inventors tried building a pumping engine powered by the explosive force of gunpowder. An English military engineer, Capt. Thomas Savery, and his chief helper, Thomas Newcomen, an iron-monger, experimented with the explosive force of steam. The result, in 1698, was the first steam-operated mine pump.

By 1725 steam engines having cylinders, pistons, automatic controls, and safety valves were at work in many mines. Meanwhile, a pressing new need, an even greater one, was becoming evident.

With better roads, people began traveling more. Farmers hauled their produce into towns; tradesmen expanded their markets to the country. The demand grew for better carts, wagons, carriages, draft animals. All of these demands meant more factories, more travel, more transportation of ores, timber, coal, and other goods. The pace of progress was such that the horse and ox were overwhelmed by the weight and volume of the things they were required to haul. A better means of transport, a wholly different means, must be found. Horse-drawn transport had become as antiquated as fire setting.

Mines felt the need first, for here the increase of output brought about by gunpowder was resulting in loads of ore almost too heavy for horses. Early measures to ease the burden were primitive: logs were laid in the ruts worn into mine roads by the groaning wooden wheels of coal and ore wagons. On mine properties around Newcastle, England, however, the operators devised a new kind of road to connect their mines with water transport on the River Tyne. They laid short logs in the roadbed at intervals of two or three feet and spiked onto these crossties two parallel lines of narrow planks just a wagon's width apart. The wooden rims of wagon wheels were grooved to fit over the plank rails. This tramway, as it was called, looked like a huge ladder laid on the ground, but it enabled one draft horse, bred to enormous size, to pull a load weighing up to thirteen tons.

This was the first railroad!

The wooden rails frayed and splintered, however, under the heavy loads. To stop that, the planks were sheathed with iron plates. Then the iron plates caused the wooden wheels to fray and splinter. About 1734 iron wheels were introduced.

The iron wheels now cracked the iron rail plates. That difficulty was overcome in 1767 by the introduction of solid iron rails, and also by another innovation! Loads were distributed among smaller wagons and the wagons were coupled together in trains. The modern railway was now complete except that its power was still the horse.

The horse railroads dominated the mining scene of the British Isles and Europe for nearly a century, while in the mines the dull explosions of gunpowder and the chugging of mine pumps mingled in mounting chorus. The mines of Wales, alone, by 1800 had nearly a hundred and fifty miles of railways used solely for coal and ore. They were far too busy to haul goods or people.

The cry rose for railways not limited to the mining industry. The first such road, the Surrey iron railway, was authorized by the British Parliament in 1801 and completed in 1803. The iron rails extended from Wandsworth, a borough of London, to the town of Croydon. The distance of almost ten miles was covered by the first passenger train, drawn by a beribboned horse, in about two hours. The epochal event stirred the nation.

The time was now ripe for the entry of the steam locomotive. Indeed, the locomotive was overdue. Steam mine pumps had been developed for new uses. They were now pumping water from lakes and streams into towns, dredging rivers and harbors, turning factory wheels. The era of modern industry had begun. Every advance had added to the burdens of transport to the point where continued use of horses on railways was a reproach to men's inventive skill.

As it turned out, another quarter century was to elapse before the steam locomotive came to being. Why the delay?

Here we come to one of the strangest of all episodes in the record of explosives, and to one of the most contrary of all the world's great inventors, James Watt. Watt was a stubborn Scot. He began life poor both in pocket and in health, but when the first horse-drawn train of the Surrey railway plodded into London to the cheers of thousands, his name was the greatest in steam power. He was sixty-seven years old, and had done more than any other man to make Great Britain the leader in steam's development. Beginning as an instrument repairman, he had improved the Newcomen engine, which had succeeded and outmoded Savery's.

Yet if Watt cheered that first passenger train at all, it was the beribboned horse that aroused his enthusiasm. He was unalterably opposed to steam's being employed for power on either railroads or highways. His reason was stated with the authority of the foremost expert speaking the last word: steam under pressure was a most dangerous explosive, a rival of gunpowder, and no engine in which steam was highly compressed was safe! The master inventor wanted no repetition, in steam power, of gunpowder's bloody past.

At Birmingham, England, Watt and his manufac-
turer-partner, Matthew Boulton, operated what had
become the largest steam engine plant in the world.
They built stationary engines, of one basic type, for
every purpose. Every Boulton and Watt engine was a
low-pressure engine safe enough to be used in a church.
The pressure under which the steam was compressed
was kept almost to that of atmospheric pressure.

An engine capable of moving a steam wagon over
the road under its own power required higher com-
pression — higher than atmospheric pressure. And if
a steam wagon was to pull a train of other wagons the
pressure had to be raised yet more, or, as Mr. Watt
believed, to a point of explosive danger.

He was not guessing about the danger. Much better
and stronger metal cylinders that would not burst under an explosion of gunpowder had been cast. Indeed,
except for the progress made in casting cannon, the
development of steam power at that stage of men's
knowledge might never have been possible. In cannon,
however, the gunpowder charge still had to be carefully calculated to suit the strength of the gun, and,
similarly, the charge of steam had to be limited to suit
the cylinder. So strongly did Watt feel about the
danger of high-pressure steam that he had petitioned
the British Parliament to pass a law prohibiting its use
in any form.

Nineteen years before the Surrey iron railway began
operating, or as early as 1784, Watt had patented what,

had he chosen to build it, could have been the first steam-driven vehicle. In 1803 the plans were gathering dust in a drawer of his desk at Birmingham. His assistants were not permitted to do any work on them, and the plans served the further purpose, under the patent law, of discouraging any work by others, for it was widely known that Watt jealously guarded his patent rights.

If James Watt had been merely a crank, his opposition to high-pressure engines would have verged on the laughable. It is said that he even went to the extreme, when he bought a home, of insisting upon a clause in the deed that barred any steam vehicle from approaching the property under any pretext. But crank or not, Watt was his day's Edison of steam power. His warnings, echoing those that had marked gunpowder's march, became a chorus in which people joined by the tens of thousands. The powerful horse trade united behind him.

However, the need for steam power was great, and every low-pressure engine that Boulton and Watt hitched to the wheels of factories accentuated it. In a dozen nations, despite the risks, men experimented with steam at pressures that Watt pronounced dangerous. There were accidents. Men died. But the work did not stop.

One of these experimenters was Richard Trevithick, the six-foot-two-inch son of a tin mine manager in Cornwall, England. Not much of a student, but the

champion wrestler and weight lifter of his school,
young Trevithick proved that he was also a born
mechanic. Moreover, he throve on opposition.

When twenty-five years old he invented a mine
pump that, in Cornwall, was hailed as being as good as
Boulton and Watt's best. At twenty-seven he directly
challenged Watt's low-pressure pump by building a
higher-pressure pump that performed better.

Thus arousing the famous man's ire, Trevithick did
not hesitate to arouse it further. Applying high-pressure principles to motive power, he built the first steam
carriage to carry passengers on a highway on Christmas
Eve, 1801. A year or so later, a second Trevithick
machine was demonstrated in London, making a sensational run along Oxford Street, from Leather Lane
to Paddington, at the height of the shopping hours.

Nothing like this machine had ever before been seen
on wheels. The thing was almost as big as a small
house. The front wheels were of stagecoach size, the
rear wheels a good twelve feet in diameter. To these
gigantic rear wheels, power was transmitted by cogwheels from an engine mounted on a rear platform.
The engine looked like an enormous bass drum, and
from it protruded an iron smokestack that towered to
the height of a second story window.

The body of the carriage was raised about six feet
above the ground level in order to make space for the
big cogwheels underneath it. The body was of stagecoach type, with three windows on each side, and it
seated eight people. From an open seat in front, the

coachman's box, Trevithick steered by means of a long lever. His partner, Andrew Vivian, rode standing on a low platform in the rear. There he could attend to the engine and keep an eye on the safety valve.

Lumbering and ungainly though it was, the Trevithick steam carriage not only ran, but also could go more than ten miles an hour with eight people aboard.

And Trevithick was not done with his defiance of James Watt. He followed his London triumph with a second: a railway locomotive powered by steam. In its trial run in 1804, on a railway of the Pen-y-darran mines of the great Merthyr Tydfil coal and ore center in Wales, his locomotive pulled wagons loaded with twenty tons of iron. Trevithick scored further triumphs. He invented the first steam-driven threshing machine for farmers. He foresaw the tractor. But this remarkable man died in 1833 — penniless, beaten, and unhonored.

Other rebel inventors joined him before his death in the fight to get high-pressure steam engines accepted for highway transportation. Several lines of steam-driven stagecoaches actually began operations in England. One introduced a regular passenger service between Cheltenham and Gloucester, and in good weather its steam coaches made speeds up to fourteen miles an hour. The automobile industry, though it was yet to earn that name, seemed to be well under way.

But though James Watt died in 1819 at the age of eighty-three, the outcry he had started against steam's explosive dangers did not die. Horse dealers and breeders, their business threatened, magnified the outcry into a national issue involving the public safety.

The clamor against steam on roads pervaded every hamlet, and most homes in Britain. Protest meetings were held. Local governing bodies barred steam engines from their highways and streets by laws or by measures that had the same effect. Road use tolls were exorbitant. Steam stage lines were forced to keep their speeds below four miles an hour, less than that of the horse-drawn stages. Every steam coach was required to carry an operating crew of three men, plus a flagman who went ahead on foot warning everybody of the approaching menace to life, limb, and property.

Our roads today swarm with motorcars using fuels more explosive than steam. To us the furor of Trevithick's day may seem to have been ridiculous, but it forced all power-driven vehicles, right down to tricycles, off the public roads and streets of Great Britain and kept them off for fifty years. As late as 1881 the British high courts upheld the prohibitions.

Forced off the highways, the steam locomotive — it was already so known — had no place to go except to the railways, and to the railways it went.

Mining men, who had been operating horse railways for decades and blasting with gunpowder even longer, were not awed by the risks of explosions — accidents were a routine hazard of their industry. To miners, the real test of the steam locomotive was: could it move coal and ore more cheaply than the horse did?

The man who did most toward making the answer

to that question positive beyond doubt was George Stephenson.

The son of an English miner, Stephenson's first job was to help his father fire the engine of a mine pump in the Newcastle mining district. At the age of eighteen he was given a pump engine of his own to attend. It was a Boulton and Watt engine, and some printed instructions came with it.

Young Stephenson could not read. He decided to go to night school and learn how, if only to read those instructions. That accomplished, he went on with his studies at night to make himself an engineer, and he eventually became the most successful builder of locomotives at the critical juncture when the mining industry, indeed all industry, was most pressed by the need for better transport. Thus, by a quirk, it was Watt who unwittingly inspired the career of Trevithick's most notable successor.

Stephenson's first locomotive, which he named *My Lord*, made its trial run in 1814 over the railway of the mine that employed him. *My Lord* was able, with much puffing of steam and black smoke, to pull eight wagonloads of coal, weighing thirty tons, up a slight grade at four miles an hour. That was a good start, but not good enough: the cost was too high when compared to the cost of horse power.

The inventor went back to his books. Seven years more of study and grubbing out a lean living brought his big chance. Parliament in 1821 granted a charter for the building of a new railway, the Stockton and

Darlington line, which its promoters envisioned as a carrier of coal, ores, and heavy freight only. With three short spurs, the line was to have more than thirty-eight miles of single track. Horses were to supply the power.

Here, at forty years of age, Stephenson proved that he possessed a talent that husky Dick Trevithick had lacked: the ability to talk convincingly and to muster figures and facts. He did not merely talk himself into the post of chief engineer for the construction of the new railway; once in that post he persuaded the promoters to switch from horses to steam. They ended up by giving him a free hand.

The completed railway was opened on September 27, 1825. The great and elite of Britain were present. When Stephenson himself climbed into the driver's seat of the locomotive, it seemed to the mass of onlookers that he was daring an impossible feat. The train hitched to his iron horse consisted of thirty-four freight wagons loaded to a gross weight of ninety tons! The locomotive, however, was no longer the ungainly contraption that twenty-three years earlier had startled the London shoppers. For one thing, the engine and smokestack were in front.

Because of fears that the boiler might explode when the pressure rose, the crowds were held back by a platoon of police. A signalman bearing a red flag was assigned to go ahead of the moving train, but he was mounted on a fast horse, evidence of expected high speeds.

The last speech was made, the ribbon of tape cut.

Stephenson opened the throttle. The iron beast belched and coughed. There was a breathless pause, and then the long train began to creep ahead. The belching of the engine became a steady pant as the ninety-ton train gathered momentum. Even the strongest doubters joined in the cheers, for this was history being made.

On rolled the train. Well before the midway point the signalman, his horse exhausted, was replaced by a second fast horseman. On one section of the line officials clocked the train's speed at fifteen miles an hour. On less favorable sections of the track it roared along at a steady twelve miles an hour.

By October, so loud was the public demand for an extension of train service to passenger traffic that the Stockton and Darlington added a coach, named *Experiment,* to one of the daily runs. Stephenson had it ready awaiting the request. The coach carried six people inside, but from fifteen to twenty people piled aboard outside. The round trip between terminals was made in two hours, the fare was a shilling, and up to fourteen pounds of baggage per passenger was carried free.

Next, the incredible happened. The price of coal at Darlington, which had been eighteen shillings a ton, was reduced by more than one half!

Yet much of the public still continued to be hostile to steam power. Not until 1830 was the future of steam railways fully assured, when Stephenson wiped out the last of the opposition.

Against the almost unanimous opinion of Britain's leading engineers that it could not be done, he built a railway that linked the great industrial complex about Manchester with the port of Liverpool. The line crossed Chat Moss, a dreary, roadless area near Manchester that was then a peat bog as shaky underfoot as jelly. The ex-pump tender bridged the bog. And that feat behind him, he undertook a second feat just as daring — to win the most prized reward of his lifetime.

He had an only son, Robert, who was born in 1803 when the father was struggling to educate himself at night, when frequently the price of a book was hunger. George Stephenson had made every sacrifice to send Robert to one of England's best schools, and later to science classes at the University of Edinburgh. Robert was his father's partner in surveying Chat Moss, and in the crucial test on which rested the future of steam power.

As chief engineer of the Manchester-Liverpool line, the elder Stephenson put aside that advantage when it came to selecting the line's locomotives. He insisted upon a competition, open to anybody, by which exacting tests would decide which locomotives would be purchased. A prize of five hundred pounds was offered by the railway to the winner of the tests which would be judged by impartial engineers.

Three engine builders entered the contest. Two of the entries broke down before completing the competition. The third, a locomotive called *The Rocket,* was the entry of George and Robert Stephenson, father and son.

The Rocket was not long in proving that the sacrifices made for the son's scientific training were not wasted. This jointly designed locomotive incorporated ideas that were to become the standards for steam power over the next century — until steam gave way to Diesel oil power on railroads.

The distance between Manchester and Liverpool is thirty-five miles. Drawing two loaded passenger coaches, *The Rocket* on first trial made the trip in forty-eight minutes. That represented an average speed of forty-four miles an hour. Men had never before traveled that fast and lived.

When the railway was formally opened in 1830, eight Rocket-type engines were put into regular service, and soon an improved engine, *The Planet,* joined the fleet designed and built by father and son. In spite of its explosive power, high-pressure steam had come to stay.

During the next fifty years the steam railway movement swept around the globe. Though high-pressure boilers did blow up now and then, and still do, most of the world forgot entirely that steam had ever been looked upon as an explosive at all. It had become a daily tool of a rapidly industrializing civilization, and occasional accidents were taken in stride.

That quelling of James Watt's old fears brought about an accompanying reversal of thinking about gunpowder that, had Friar Roger Bacon been alive, surely would have shocked him beyond belief.

The great onward surge in railroad building introduced wholly new problems in mining — in rock removal, tunneling, mountain moving; in the supplying of iron, copper, and other metals, all on a scale formerly undreamed of. Soon gunpowder itself, mightiest of all tools, was staggering under the vast new burden of work, even as the horse had staggered.

The sailing ship was being replaced by steam. Water wheels were being supplanted by engines. Now, on the new railroads, in the mines, even in the barracks of the world's armies, a rising complaint was heard: explosives of a much greater power than gunpowder's were needed to do the work that was to be done. Gunpowder was now as outdated as were Mr. Watt's notions about high pressures in steam power. The search was on for high explosives.

Chapter 8

SUPEREXPLOSIVES

THE search was on, and never was there a stranger one. There were no clarion calls, no glittering rewards, no campaigns for funds — just muffled blasts in mines and the rising tempo of steam-driven wheels, the challenge of broadening opportunity to all men.

The seekers were Swedes, Frenchmen, Germans, Swiss, Italians, British. What united them was a yen to learn and add to the common knowledge. With few exceptions these men toiled after their usual day's work was done, contrived their own equipment, bought their own supplies. They asked for no pay, no notices in the press.

Outside of musty textbooks, most of their names were to remain unknown. But their discoveries, when joined link by link, were to produce a chain of vaster changes in the world than did all the conquests of Alexander the Great, Julius Caesar, and Napoleon.

The first step in any search for the unknown is to learn what others earlier in the field have discovered, so let us quickly look back from the time when the steam railroads began spreading out everywhere. Paralleling the development of steam power, chemistry had emerged from the dark alleys of alchemy and set up some enduring milestones.

About the time that Savery and Newcomen were tinkering with their first steam mine pump, an English clergyman of curious bent was tinkering with the soft, bituminous coal of his native Yorkshire. The Rev. Dr. John Clayton never was at loss for an interest when not devoted to his Bible and church. He was at once an authority on the plant life, red Indians, and other "observables" in the faraway colony of Virginia. He was an experimenter of boundless curiosity. What made coal burn? Of what was it composed? The tireless rector explored those puzzling questions.

"I got some coal," he wrote later, "which I distilled in a Retort in an open Fire. At first there came only *Phlegm,* afterwards a black Oil, and then likewise a *Spirit* arose, which I could noways condense, but it forced my Lute, or broke my Glasses."

Which was to say that the "Spirit," or gas, upon continued heating blew out the cork or burst the bottle or retort in which it was held. It was highly explosive.

Dr. Clayton filled a good many pig's bladders, first squeezed and voided of air, with this "Spirit." "And when I had a Mind to divert Strangers or Friends, I have frequently taken one of these Bladders, and pricking a Hole therein with a Pin, and compressing gently the Bladder near the Flame of a Candle till it once took Fire, it would then continue flaming till all the Spirit was compressed out of the Bladder."

The rector had no idea that he was playing with the raw materials of perhaps a dozen industries of the future, but he was. Among them: gas for lighting, heat, and cooking; dyes; drugs; antiseptics; perfumes; photographic chemicals; fertilizers; plastics; and, by no means least, high explosives that would make gunpowder look puny.

As the decades passed, others took up where Dr. Clayton had left off. His "Phlegm" was identified as ammonia liquor, his "black Oil" as coal tar, and his "Spirit" as coal gas. The presence of ammonia in coal pointed to its kinship with saltpeter. But remember coal tar, for we shall meet it again in finer guise. It is probably the most valuable raw material known to the organic chemist.

We come next, almost a century after Clayton, to the picturesque village of Köping, which is tucked in a cove of Lake Malar in Sweden. The estates of Stockholm's rich and great then dotted the miles of lakeshore, and still do; but we pass them all by for a tiny drugstore in Köping. Its proprietor from 1775 to 1786, when he died at the age of forty-four, was Karl Wilhelm Scheele.

Scheele was a thin, shy, apologetic little man who was always pressed for time and money. He had so little of both that he felt he could not afford to marry until two days before he died, when he did just to make sure that his widow, after years of waiting for him, would have the drugstore, at least. His neighbors, calling on him for medicines and pills and often finding

that he had forgotten their prescription entirely, must
have put him down as a failure. He did not own, it
seemed, so much as a single unfrayed shirt.

It was after his drugstore door was closed and locked
for the night that Karl Scheele became the man that
he really was. Then, retreating to his combined laboratory and living quarters in the store's rear, he lit his
candle, cooked and ate his frugal meal, sat down at his
stone workbench, and became a bold, sure, confident
explorer.

He was one of the greatest chemists who ever lived.
Working with apparatus that he made himself, often
half-frozen by the winter night's cold, he made discoveries that were to guide researchers in medicine,
dentistry, photography, explosives, and other fields
right down to our own day.

He was the first to identify chlorine and fluorine,
two chemical elements. Of special interest to us, in
1774 he separated from saltpeter its "fire-air," or the
vital element, oxygen. And he created glycerin.

Among Scheele's ailments were badly chapped hands.
He found that glycerin was a good remedy for them,
and thereafter Köping's schoolboys flocked to his store
for some of the sweet, syrupy hand lotion that he cooked
from hog's lard, or butter, or one of the vegetable oils.
However, though he carefully analyzed the properties
of glycerin, he never foresaw that someday it would
shake and shock the world. That discovery he left
to the next generation.

Other chemists, each only a little less brilliant than Scheele, lived at the same time.

Henry Cavendish was the son of an English lord, the brother of a duke, and one of England's richest men. Yet he was as shy in manner and shabby of dress as was the little Köping druggist. Besides, he stammered, though not in his chemical researches. He was the first man to identify hydrogen, one of the two elements of water.

Suspecting that hydrogen was present in moist air, he passed electric sparks through moist air compressed in a glass vessel, and to his surprise got a colorless, strongly fuming fluid that he recognized as nitric acid. This semiexplosive liquid had long been known, but formerly it had been obtained by distilling saltpeter and sulphuric acid.

His discovery that the atmosphere also yields nitric acid indicated that the explosive gases of gunpowder could be free in the air in boundless supply, awaiting only the ingenuity of man to capture them. The identity of the first of those gases, nitrogen, was discovered by another Englishman, Daniel Rutherford, in 1772.

Next came Scheele's discovery of oxygen, a feat that was duplicated by Joseph Priestly, another Yorkshire-born clergyman who outranged Dr. Clayton in his interests. Priestley was at once a chemist, philosopher, author, political reformer, and scholarly student of six languages including Hebrew and Arabic. His preachings were so virulent that he was forced in old age to flee England for America. He settled down quietly at Northumberland, Pennsylvania, where he died.

As a chemical explorer Priestley carried research in oxygen a long step beyond Scheele's beginning. He was the first to suspect that this colorless, odorless gas is the essential element of the air that we breathe, a supporter of all animal and vegetable life as well as of heat, light, fire, and all forms of combustion.

These and other discoveries lent a new force to scientific effort. How mighty was that new force we may judge by looking back to Roger Bacon's day when science, such as it was, groped in a fog of superstition, suspicion, and indifference to change.

Learned though he was, one of the great thinkers, Friar Bacon had never heard of nitrogen, oxygen, or hydrogen. Then only ten of the elements were known: iron, copper, lead, gold, silver, tin, mercury, zinc, sulphur, and carbon. All ten had been found before the birth of Christ. Centuries had passed without the discovery of a single new element!

Bacon's own century, the 13th, added arsenic to the known list; the 15th century, bismuth and antimony. About 1669 a German, curious about the mysterious glow to be seen in saltpeter sheds at night, discovered that it was given off by the element, phosphorus.

There was another standstill until 1735, when two new elements were brought to light: cobalt, the nickel-like element of magnet steel; and platinum, the rare metal that is more precious than gold.

When Cavendish and Scheele and their generation

of chemists went to work, the total of all elements known to mankind was sixteen. Only six had been added in some five hundred years. Suddenly, in 1766, when hydrogen was identified, chemistry began to make major discoveries at the rate of one every two or three years. By 1842, just six hundred years after Bacon had revealed the simple formula for gunpowder, fifty-six elements, well over half of all that we know today, were known.

Uranium was known. Another druggist-chemist, Martin Klaproth, the Scheele of Germany, had roasted that radioactive element from pitchblende in 1789. The atomic theory had been advanced by John Dalton, the Quaker son of a poor English millworker, as early as 1803.

Any chemist of 1842 was richer in knowledge, and so of greater potential, than had been Bacon or Cavendish or Scheele or any of the older pioneers. And it was fortunate that was true. Progress was moving at a pace that would have left the old leaders aghast.

The steam railways were reaching out from every large center in Europe. Britain alone was to have almost 6700 miles of track in operation by 1850. Americans were adding track at a rate of 2000 miles yearly; the United States was to have an amazing 9000 miles by the mid-century.

Gunpowder was doing its best to help horses, mules, plows, scrapers, picks, shovels, and human brawn to clear the miles of new right of way; to blast the tens of thousands of tons of hard rock required as ballast for the roadbeds; to open tunnels and cuts through mountains; to mine iron for bridges, rails, cars, engines, and the new industries that steam power made possible.

But gunpowder's best was not good enough. The explosive that had recast war and civilization faltered in hard rock. It "pushed" the rock out in large chunks which then had to be broken up by hand with sledge hammers. Needed was an explosive that would loosen hard rock and also shatter it, that would thunder its way through any barrier, even granite.

Gunpowder had other limitations that were made more apparent by advances in the development of firearms and the growing scope of war. Powder grains were now treated with an oil or grease to keep them from absorbing moisture; this oil, plus the charcoal in the mixture of saltpeter and sulphur, caused such clouds of smoke in battle that soldiers could not see. Hands, faces, and uniforms became filthy in the sooty air. The powder so dirtied the bores of guns that they had to be cleaned repeatedly; this fault had seriously delayed the introduction of breachloading, repeating rifles; machine guns; and rifled long-range cannon.

Yes, the search was on for a mountain wrecker in the cause of peace; for a clean-burning, smokeless explosive in the cause of war. Times had changed; the demon that once had seemed to threaten the world's doom was now much too tame!

Two major tasks faced the chemists in their search, and each was revolutionary. The first was to create a wholly new chemical compound, a single material, in which the molecules of oxygen, nitrogen, and carbon, the key elements, were joined in such a way that they would explode instantly when fired. The second was to find a source of carbon that was superior to charcoal.

A field new to inventive vision, that of chemical creation or synthesis, was to be invaded. Nature's ways were to be converted to man's prescribed purposes. Compounds not found in nature had been made before, but purely as a result of exploratory work without plan. Glycerin was such a compound. Scheele had produced it without having any use for it in mind except as a hand lotion.

This new search was aimed in advance at supplying a known need, at inventing an explosive that had specific qualities that were lacking in the old mixture of saltpeter, sulphur, and carbon.

The chemists at last realized that gunpowder was merely a mixture, not a chemical compound at all. The mixing of the three materials, however finely they were grained, did not rearrange their molecules. In effect, the key elements continued to occupy separate rooms. The result, when gunpowder was fired, was a delay in the elements' getting together; the explosion was not instantaneous. That delay, though of less than a split second, made gunpowder a "low," not a "high," explosive.

It was easy to reduce some of the delay. The chemists distilled saltpeter and sulphuric acid, and got nitric acid, as we have noted. A drop of this fuming liquid will sear one's skin like molten metal. It is so viciously corrosive it will eat into steel. In nitric acid are linked the molecules of nitrogen and oxygen.

The next step toward forming the desired compound was to join the linked nitrogen-oxygen molecules with carbon molecules. That also was easy, because carbon is one of the elements most willing to unite with others. But before taking that concluding step of synthesis, the chemists had to find a carbon source that did not have charcoal's faults, one that would not add smoke and dirt to the explosion. They were decades in accomplishing that task.

Carbon is everywhere. It comprises the main building block of nature in forming the structures of trees and plants, animals and people, all living or organic things. It is abundant in oils and gases, coal, diamonds, and some minerals. But in all of its infinite forms carbon is rarely, if ever, alone. Its congenial eagerness to combine with other molecules is, to the chemist, at once a virtue and a hazard. It may introduce wholly undesirable elements into the compound that is sought.

At that time little was known about the structure of any of the carbon-rich materials. Organic chemistry was in its formative stage, and the explorers had to write their rules as they learned from their failures. They began combining nitric acid with every kind of promising carbon-rich substance that was plentiful and cheap. If they succeeded they foresaw the demand for huge quantities of the new explosive, which made availability and cost guiding factors.

How many engaged in the work, how many paid for

the risks they took with injuries if not their lives, we do not know, for the developing new science recorded only what they learned. The compounding process was described by a new verb, to *nitrate*, and it is a common verb with chemists today.

They nitrated sugar, starch, flour, paper, linen, cotton, finely ground coal, sawdust, chalk. They studied the ancient wildfires, as had Friar Bacon, and tried nitrating turpentine, naptha, quicklime. They experimented with Scheele's chlorine, with the good Dr. Clayton's coal tar, and learned that in coal tar was a chemical empire waiting to be conquered.

And they produced explosives of many kinds. Some were weak, some blew up at the slightest cause, some emitted deadly fumes, some had qualities that gunpowder lacked. But none of them proved to be the superexplosive — until 1846.

That year should be written in red letters in any history of mankind. For then, in Switzerland, a professor of chemistry created guncotton, and in Italy another professor of chemistry created nitroglycerin.

Both compounds exploded cleanly, both were smokeless, both had tremendous power. Here at once were two superexplosives.

According to a story widely told at the time, guncotton was discovered in a kitchen. German-born Herr Professor Christian Friedrich Schönbein, who taught at the University of Basel, often did his experimenting at home, much to the annoyance of his wife. The kitchen became his laboratory when she was out.

One evening, while he was distilling nitric and sulphuric acids in a flask on the stove, his flask broke. He grabbed the nearest thing at hand, his wife's cotton apron, to wipe up the mess. Then, to hide the accident from her, he carefully washed the apron in water and hung it up to dry near the hot stove.

Shortly afterwards he heard an explosive puff and saw the apron vanish instantly in flames. Highly excited, he hunted up another cotton cloth and repeated the chemical treatment by which he had nitrated the apron. After he had again washed out all visible evidence of what he had done, the piece of cloth appeared to be that and no more, totally unchanged. He cut off a strip and touched it with a lighted match. It was instantly consumed by a flash of flame and left no ash or smoke, only a slightly acrid odor.

Whether or not the professor made his discovery in the kitchen or elsewhere, there is no doubt that he was at once aware of its military importance. He first tested it in a gun, in which he replaced gunpowder with a tight little wadded strip of his highly inflammable cotton cloth. The results of repeated firing tests were so good that he named his new explosive *Schiessbaumwolle,* the German for "shooting tree-wool," or guncotton.

The newspapers hailed guncotton as the successor to gunpowder in firearms and cannon.

Seeing a fortune ahead, Herr Schönbein hurried to Berlin to offer his secret formula to the Prussian army.

He was unable to get a hearing, so he rushed to Vienna and promptly sold the formula to Austria. Before another month was out he was in London and sold the formula to England, where it was patented in the name of John Taylor.

Soon it was obvious that other chemists, widely separated, had been on the verge of discovering guncotton or a similar explosive. By December, 1846, not only Austria and England, but also France, Germany, and Russia were building guncotton plants.

America remained aloof. The Du Ponts of Delaware were the largest manufacturers of gunpowder in the United States, and the company's head, Alfred du Pont, scented trouble. "The discovery," he ruled, "is brilliant and such as to create astonishment, but the introduction of guncotton in common use must be the work of time."

America was to be guided by that decision for the next forty-odd years.

The wisdom of it was soon confirmed in England. The English gungotton plant at Faversham, near London, was hastily erected, workers were hastily trained. In July, 1847, the plant exploded. Twenty men were killed.

In quick succession similar explosions occurred in Russia, Germany, and France. Only Austria persevered in the attempt to manufacture guncotton and adapt it to artillery, until 1862. That year the first of two Austrian plants blew up and many men were killed; soon the second had a similarly disastrous accident. Austria now abandoned guncotton as being too dangerous to manufacture.

But the chemists kept working and kept learning. We shall hear of guncotton again.

Nitroglycerin, the second superexplosive of 1846, got none of guncotton's initial acclaim; it was barely noted outside scientific circles. Its inventor was Ascanio Sobrero, a studious, modest professor of industrial chemistry at Italy's University of Turin. He had been a medical student, and then turned to chemistry as a developing science that promised much for mankind's good. His interest was in speeding progress, not war.

Sobrero was thirty-four years old when he began the experiments that were to lead, later, to a monument built in Turin to his memory. The statue shows him as a handsome man of dreamy face, flowing hair, and pointed beard. He taught that science should not be used for personal profit or dishonorable ends.

Glycerin was a common remedy for chapped hands, and Sobrero kept some of it in his laboratory for that use. He knew that, coming from fats or oils, glycerin is carbon-rich. One day, in a curious mood, he added some of the hand lotion, drop by drop, to a mixture of nitric and sulphuric acids, stirring as he did so and being careful to keep the mixture well cooled for safety. Then he poured the combined chemicals into a basin of water. A pale yellow oil separated and sank to the bottom of the basin.

The oil had a sweet, burning taste; he learned by

further tests that it was decidedly poisonous. Cautiously, he heated a small amount of it. A vapor arose, and his head began to ache violently. When the heat exceeded 130°C., the vapor became red in color and an explosion sent Sobrero reeling from the room.

Uneasy over his discovery, he said nothing about it except to a few close friends. Week after week, after his classes had been dismissed for the day, he experimented with the new oil alone, to make sure that nobody else got hurt. He soaked it up in blotting paper, lighted a piece of the paper, and it burned in a flash without smoke. He placed a bit of the blotter on an anvil and struck it with a hammer; it detonated with such force that the windows rattled.

He placed a drop of the oil in a heavy glass bowl and heated the bowl slowly with a spirit lamp. The bowl was shattered into a thousand bits by the explosion. Again, he measured an even more minute quantity of the oil into a test tube and passed the tube over the flame of his spirit lamp in a quick motion. The explosion was instant and so fierce that his hands and face were cut by the flying glass.

The longer he tested the oil the more fearful he became of it. Usually he wound up his tests with that splitting headache he had first noticed. He was able to formulate no certain rules for this explosive except one: that it was highly dangerous and of a power he could not measure.

Almost a year passed before he agreed to publish the details of his experiments for the guidance of his fellow scientists. He warned that nitroglycerin was much too treacherous and unpredictable for anyone to attempt its manufacture until more was known about it, that meanwhile the world would do well to leave it alone.

Ascanio Sobrero went back to his teaching. During the next fifteen years the pale yellow oil was little more than a scientific curiosity. A daring researcher in medicine found a limited use for it as a heart stimulant, to which he gave the name of "oil of glonoin." That was all.

Then came startling news. Two Swedes, father and son, had tested nitroglycerin in blasting hard rock, with results so promising that they planned to manufacture the high explosive on large scale. It was to be sold under the trade name of Nobel's Blasting Oil.

Sobrero read, and said a silent prayer.

Chapter 9

DYNAMITE

THE name linked with "blasting oil" was that of one of the strangest of all families, and also of one of the strangest of all inventive geniuses, Alfred Bernard Nobel.

The family's head, Emmanuel Nobel, was first to bring its name to public attention. He was a self-educated Swedish peasant whose interests ranged from architecture to devices for blowing up ships at sea. One of his ideas was to train seals to tow mines or floating cases of explosives into the pathway of hostile war vessels.

In 1837, when thirty-five years old, he turned to torpedoes and invented one that not only wrecked his home in Stockholm, but also broke so many of his neighbors' windowpanes that he was visited by the police. They warned him to leave Stockholm if he intended to persist in such work.

The notice thus gained led the Russian ambassador to Sweden to invite Emmanuel Nobel to operate a torpedo factory for the Czar in Russia. When the Crimean War broke out in 1856, Nobel torpedoes — said to be loaded with nitroglycerin or guncotton, possibly both — frightened away a British fleet that threatened Russia's main naval base.

But Russia lost the war. The Czar lost interest in torpedoes and Nobel. At sixty, he returned to Sweden, bankrupt in money but not in schemes, for Nobel's Blasting Oil had opened a new, exciting road to fortune.

It was in this atmosphere of daily risks, with pots of explosive chemicals fuming in the kitchen or in a back-yard shed, that Emmanuel Nobel's four sons — Robert, Ludwig, Alfred, and Oscar — were reared. The family was closely knit. While it was sometimes hungry and the roof was never safe, there was no dearth of bold dreams.

The two older sons, Robert and Ludwig, went on to amass great fortunes in the Baku oil fields of Russia, and always reserved a share of their money for the others. The two younger sons, Alfred and Oscar, be-came their father's right and left arms, though for Alfred the role of bold adventurer seemed odd indeed. Born in 1833, he was frail and sickly, and with such a weak back that he walked with a stoop, appearing al-most dwarflike. In later years he wore a black stubbly beard that added to his dwarfish look. He complained all of his life of gout, rheumatism, and heart trouble, for which he took endless remedies and hot mineral baths.

Too sickly as a boy to attend school, Alfred's early education came largely from his mother. Always on hand were those messes of fuming chemicals and his

father's unflagging zeal for world-changing inventions
which somehow never quite came off. While in Russia,
Alfred learned to speak and write Russian fluently.
Later he mastered French and German. It was hard
to keep him away from the torpedo factory, so he was
sent to the United States to spend four years with his
father's friend, John Ericsson, the eminent Swedish-
American engineer and inventor. He came home afire
with America's enormous potential in mining, and with
English added to his store of languages.

When Nobel's Blasting Oil set Europe talking during the early 1860's, it was still in Emmanuel's usual
"not-quite-right" stage. But Alfred, nearing thirty, was
now both an excellent chemist and a very good mechanical engineer. He shied from social affairs, never
married, never wasted time on hobbies. His all-con-
suming concern was to put high explosives to work.

Swedish bankers ridiculed the thought of risking any
money in a Nobel nitroglycerin factory. Alfred went
to France. There the Emperor Napoleon III was eager
to encourage any venture that might strengthen the
rest of Europe against the rising might of Germany.
Through his influence, the stooped, frail chemist-
engineer was able to borrow a hundred thousand francs
from one of the French banks.

By 1863 the Nobel plant was a fact, at Heleneborg,
Sweden, not too far from where druggist Scheele had
sold his glycerin to school children. The plant was
small. Its entire working force was a mechanic, old
Emmanuel; and Oscar, then nineteen years old. Close

by the wooden building Alfred set up a laboratory, and therein his lamp burned far into the night.

Nitroglycerin's big fault, as viewed by blasters who had tried it at the Nobels' request, was that one could never be certain about its firing. When the oil was poured into a bore hole in rock and ignited by a fuse, it was too prone to burn, not to explode. Being liquid, the oil could not be compressed, as gunpowder was, simply by tamping earth above the charge.

Alfred Nobel worked with that problem. He mixed nitroglycerin and gunpowder and fired the mixture with a fuse. The blast was good, but not good enough. It led him to float a gunpowder cartridge atop pure nitroglycerin in the bore hole, with better results. Next he substituted a percussion cap for the cartridge, and the instant answering blast told him that he was near a big discovery.

Percussion caps had been invented in 1805 by a hunt-loving Scotch minister, Alexander Forsythe, and had been used on guns for some time to fire the gunpowder charge. The metal cap, fitted over the gun's firing nipple, was usually filled with mercury fulminate, a detonator of lightninglike action that had been discovered in the course of nitrating every promising material. Later the percussion cap made the metallic gun cartridge possible.

Alfred Nobel was the first man to apply this principle, of using one kind of explosive to detonate another, to blasting. He contrived a cap in the form of a small copper tube of nitrated mercury. When ignited by a powder fuse — later, an electric spark — this cap exploded nitroglycerin surely and in comparative safety.

His blasting cap opened a field for high explosives in mining, quarrying, and roadway building that soon was to prove more vast than Emmanuel Nobel's most fanciful vision. But that veteran weaver of grand schemes was never to realize the scope of his son's achievement.

One September morning in 1864 Heleneborg was rocked by an explosion. The Blasting Oil plant near the village erupted skyward in a cyclone of shattered beams, boards, and shingles. All that was left was the shed in which Alfred had his laboratory. He was thrown to the floor unhurt, amid a crash of broken glass and chemicals.

What had caused the explosion Alfred never learned. His brother Oscar and the mechanic were killed. His father suffered a paralytic stroke from which he never recovered. He died in 1872, a dazed old man muttering of a discovery that he believed would make him dictator of the world for the next two centuries.

The Swedish government notified Alfred that henceforth he would have to do his experimenting at some spot not dangerous to human habitations. Grimly he rented a barge and moored it in the center of a lake. By night he went ashore to receive supplies from his mother, who had a bedridden wreck of a man to nurse and debts to face at home.

Alone on the barge, muffled in heavy clothing to keep himself from freezing, the son who never had been well further perfected his blasting caps. He made up caps by hand until he had filled one side of a suitcase. Padding the other side with cotton, he filled it with bottles of the blasting oil on which his fortunes rested. Then he packed a few clothes into another suitcase. A bag in each hand, stooping more than usual under the load, he set out for Germany. He went straight to the ore-rich mining region of the Harz Mountains in Hanover, where hard rock kept men sweating to break it up.

Nobel had no difficulty in finding new backers in Germany. His blasting caps and bottles of oil spoke for him eloquently in iron, copper, lead, and silver mines alike. The firm of Alfred Nobel & Company was organized. Before spring began to bud the trees about the village of Krümmel, the company's name was lettered over the gateway of a new factory there. The eldest Nobel son, Robert, came from Russia to assume charge of the plant. In a few weeks the German factory was pushing out caps and oil as fast as they could be made.

Back to Sweden went the stooped traveler, a role that was to be his henceforth. Calling no nation home in the way men normally do, he was to remain throughout life a man without a real country. Spring was also just coming into bloom in Sweden when the second sign of Alfred Nobel & Company went up over a second factory gate at Wintervicken. Not long afterward, a third sign went up in Norway.

Soon Nobel's Blasting Oil and caps were employed in their first large-scale construction job, the blasting of a railway tunnel through solid rock near Stockholm. By autumn, the anniversary of the Heleneborg disaster, these mighty rock shatterers were performing similar feats in a dozen nations, including the United States.

Eighteen years had gone by since Sobrero's warning, but both the warning and Sobrero were forgotten. Nobel assured the world that the once-feared explosive was "safe": he had but to remind doubters of the need to use a blasting cap to detonate a bore hole charged with nitroglycerin.

His humming factories sealed the pale yellow oil in zinc cans, packed the cans into wooden shipping crates, stuffed the crates with wood shavings — later with kieselguhr, a spongy clay abundant in northern Germany — and the new blaster of fabulous power traveled the highways of the world. Salesmen bragged that the cushioning of the cans was merely an extra precaution and unnecessary.

Handlers took Nobel at his word. Peasants in the Swiss Alps jolted the liquid over rough roads in two-wheel oxcarts. When the cans leaked, which they often did from rough treatment, the peasants rubbed the thick oozing oil onto their boots or used it in lieu of axle grease. Railroads and ships carried the cans as freight with no more care than they gave cans of lard. Nobel's agents called on prospective customers, as he had done, with bottles of the stuff in their carpetbags.

"Wait!" cried gunpowdermen, alarmed at the onslaught that threatened their own sales.

The wait was not long.

In November, 1865, a porter of the Wyoming Hotel

in New York City's Greenwich Village noticed a reddish smoke curling from the heavy box that for two months he had used as a seat for his bootblacking stand. The box had been left at the hotel by a German traveler who had told nobody that it contained three pounds of nitroglycerin. He apparently had forgotten it.

The porter dragged the box into the street and ran. Fortunately it was early Sunday morning and few people were about. A moment later the box exploded. The hotel and nearby houses were damaged, doors and windows smashed, several men slashed by flying pieces of glass, and a hole four feet deep was torn in the stone pavement.

That was the prelude.

On March 4, 1866, two cases of Nobel's Blasting Oil exploded in Sydney, Australia, demolishing a warehouse and surrounding buildings. Twelve men were killed.

One month later the steamship *European,* with seventy of Nobel's crated cans in her hold, together with ammunition for South American revolutionists, blew up while unloading at what is now Colòn, Panama. The damage exceeded a million dollars. Sixty dead were counted in the debris.

Barely two weeks passed before the canned death roared again. A shipment of it destined for the California gold fields wrecked the granite building of Wells, Fargo and Company in San Francisco. Ten were killed, many more injured. The shock of the blast broke windows for a quarter of a mile around.

Still later, a cargo of nitroglycerin blew up near Brussels, Belgium, killing ten.

A horrified world protested. Cities, states, and some nations, Great Britain among them, passed stringent new laws to regulate the manufacture and shipment of all high explosives. Railways and ships refused to accept any more of Nobel's cans as freight. Warehouses dumped those on hand into rivers or the sea. Before his chemistry classes in Italy, Ascanio Sobrero bowed his head in shame for having invented this destroyer.

Yet a sensational fact stood undisputed. With all its faults, nitroglycerin would do five times as much work in rock as black blasting powder, or gunpowder, and do it better. If this mountain mover could be brought under control, mankind might be freed from many of its most backbreaking tasks.

Nobel, shunned even by friends, faced the storm as he had faced the tragedy of Heleneborg. What of gunpowder's record, he asked. It, too, was red with blood and black with denunciations! He shut himself in the laboratory of the Krümmel plant and saw nobody but Robert.

The brothers realized that, because of their haste to get nitroglycerin used, impurities had been left in the oil. These, as the oil aged, had caused it to decompose and become highly dangerous, a result wholly unforeseen by them. Robert now undertook a complete overhauling of the factory methods. Alfred assumed the harder task of making the oil as safe to handle as he had believed and claimed it was.

Earlier, he had thought of making nitroglycerin less

sensitive by absorbing it into another substance, as water is absorbed by a sponge. He revived the idea. He experimented with sawdust, ground charcoal, cement, brick dust, and finally decided on kieselguhr, the earth in which he had packed his zinc cans. Kieselguhr absorbed three times its own weight in nitroglycerin.

The oil-saturated earth became like putty. He kneaded it, shaped it into a cartridge that would fit the usual bore hole, and wrapped the cartridge in waxed paper. He lighted a cartridge; it burned but did not explode. He pounded it with a hammer, and nothing happened. But the cartridge exploded instantly when fired by a blasting cap.

Over and over the brothers repeated the tests. Satisfied that they had overlooked nothing, they made up two boxes of cartridges, or "sticks" about eight inches in length. Each taking a box, they started off separately, Alfred for German mines, Robert for stone quarries. All summer they demonstrated the invention to every skeptic who would give them audience. The cushioned explosive was less powerful than nitroglycerin alone, but its brisance, or violence, was more than twenty times that of black blasting powder.

They set fire to the oil-soaked sticks to show that they burned harmlessly — a spark would explode black powder so compressed. They hurled sticks from cliffs onto rocks below, to pick them up unexploded. By October, 1866, so sure was Alfred of the safety of the new blaster under all reasonable conditions that he invited the explosives experts of Europe to come to

Germany and challenged them to make any tests they wished.

The tests lasted a week. When the last blast had been fired, the last doubting question answered, that year of disaster became also the year of Alfred Nobel's greatest victory. The verdict was unanimous: he had brought men the nearest they had yet come to attaining a manageable force capable of moving mountains!

A new word was added to all languages: *dynamite!*

Soon, the world over, dynamite was doing for mining and heavy construction what steam power was doing for transportation and manufacturing.

Nowhere was the new tool put to work more daringly than in America. The United States was emerging from the Civil War. That war had assured national unity from ocean to ocean, and had released for peace thousands of men who had learned to laugh at danger. The Far West was awaiting conquest. Its mountains were yet to be tunneled, its rivers bridged, its mighty dams built, its wealth of ores yet to be tapped.

America's first dynamite plant rose in California early in 1868. Its site was a spot called Rock House Canyon, long since lost in the bustle of a vastly expanded San Francisco. The buildings were a few unpainted shacks, the crew a glycerin nitrator, a helper, and a dozen Chinese laborers. But the venture bore the proud name of Giant Powder Company.

The plant's glycerin and kieselguhr were shipped from Germany "round the Horn." The nitric acid, and ice for the nitrating vat to keep it from fuming, were obtained in San Francisco. The Chinamen made the dynamite sticks by hand. Once a day a chemist dropped by on horseback to see if all was well.

The California Powder Works, which only lately had built an up-to-date gunpowder plant near Santa Cruz at a cost of three hundred thousand dollars, denounced the plant in Rock House Canyon in a broadside of danger warnings. The public was reminded of the Wells, Fargo tragedy of two years before. Miners were told that use of dynamite would cost them their jobs, as it was aimed at reducing the need for labor.

But soon gold miners who sought quick fortunes were using dynamite at $1.75 a pound; it was cheaper than black blasting powder at twenty cents a pound! Using gunpowder, if hard rock was struck, the rock had first to be tunneled until enough space was made to hold from three hundred to seven hundred kegs of powder. Then the powder blast would heave out the rock in chunks the size of a miner's cabin. A fourth as much dynamite got rid of the rock in a fraction of the time and shattered it into bits.

Over the state line in Nevada lay the great Comstock Lode, with mine shafts striking deep into the rocky heart of Mount Davidson. By the war's end, the Comstock mines were producing silver bullion with a coin value of fifteen million dollars yearly. Dynamite, instead of black powder, went down the Comstock shafts, and the outflow of silver more than doubled.

The crude plant in Rock House Canyon pushed its

Chinamen harder and harder to meet the soaring demands for its "Giant Powder." The penalty for the haste was a blast one late November day, 1869, that hurled the entire works skyward. Two white men and the Chinamen so busily molding up sticks vanished with the shacks.

There was only a pause, however, in the flow of dynamite to the mine shafts. A larger, safer plant went up on the sand dunes south of what is now Golden Gate Park. A larger Chinese crew manned the workbenches, and Nobel & Company sent a chemist from Germany to serve as plant superintendent.

The first twenty-three years of the Giant Powder Company in California exemplify in dramatic terms the introduction of dynamite in the United States. During that period five different plants, each bigger than the last, were wrecked by explosions, and in all eighty-three men died. But the company's capital mounted to two million dollars.

Dynamite plants soon dotted the country. Unlike Giant, most of them were independent of Nobel. Instead of using kieselguhr to absorb the nitroglycerin, they used saltpeter, charcoal, sugar, starch, wood pulp, paraffin. Many of these were "active bases" and so joined in the explosion, added to its force, whereas kieselguhr was inactive, simply a cushioning agent that did not explode. Thus a number of new dynamites of varying strength or grades were created, a notable advance. But others were deliberate evasions of the

Nobel patent. World-wide evasions kept him, embittered, appealing to court after court to protect his rights.

The vast majority of dynamite plants were humble affairs, hidden in lonely valleys beside streams. Neighbors spoke of them uneasily as "moonlighters," and gave them a wide berth. Workmen were a rough, tough lot who slept in bunks in a nearby shed. Salesmen were often ex-miners or construction "stiffs" who could neither read nor write and had never worn a white collar. But they were the pioneers of a new industry that grew and spread despite all obstacles.

Explosions, deaths, failures, frauds, arrests, lawsuits, financial panic, the fears of miners for their jobs, the full weight of the established gunpowder industry's opposition — all of these combined could not check dynamite's popularity across the United States. New and better plants rose from the debris of the destroyed ones, new and more daring men replaced those killed in accidents.

When railroads refused to carry dynamite, it was packed in trunks as "personal baggage" or in boxes labeled "Glass, Handle with Care." When warehouses refused to store the nitroglycerin-soaked sticks, they were stored in hotel rooms as "Chinaware, Fragile" and hidden in home cellars, under beds, behind saloon bars.

Salesmen with Colt revolvers belted to their hips lugged bags of dynamite into hostile mining towns and demonstrated their wares on street corners. They held the sticks between their fingers and watched them burn, pounded the wax-coated cylinders on stone sidewalks with sledge hammers, set off blasting caps with the lighted tip of a cigar touched to the end of a fuse. When nobody would buy, they gave away free blasting kits to any miner who would agree to put one to fair trial in hard rock.

And dynamite sold at $1.75 a pound, then $1.00, then fifty cents as the trickle of output became a river, swept by Great Lakes freighters into the copper and iron districts of Lake Superior. The great open-pit iron mine of the Mesabi Range in Minnesota, alone, was to use around two million pounds of dynamite yearly and to create, by 1939, the biggest man-made excavation on our earth.

Since 1864 prospectors had been whittling away at some outcroppings of quartz on a rock-ribbed hill in Montana, known as Butte Hill. In 1875 dynamite hauled by muleback opened veins of ore — copper, zinc, lead, manganese, silver — that showed that Butte Hill was one of the world's most fabulously rich deposits. So began the Anaconda Company, giant of copper, and the tapping of mineral wealth that to date has exceeded three billion dollars.

Mississippi River boats carried dynamite to St. Louis, and it was carted overland to the lead and zinc mines of Joplin, Missouri, where men became rich overnight. The wax-coated cartridges dug sewers in New York, uprooted stumps in Ohio, drained swamps in Louisiana, began furnishing millions of tons of limestone for use as flux in the smelting of iron ore and in making steel.

History records a phenomenal industrial advance in the United States following the Civil War. Between 1870 and 1890 Americans built 113,955 miles of railroads, or more than double the mileage that was built during the previous fifty years. Production of iron was quadrupled, copper output multiplied nine times, silver output increased five times. All industry seemed to have discovered seven-league boots.

The boots were dynamite!

Until dynamite made large-scale rock blasting practicable, no cement was made in America. The cost of mining nickel made it a precious metal, while the price of silver was so high that only the rich could afford to own silver knives, forks, and spoons. Most of today's common minerals were imprisoned beneath layers of impenetrable rock until dynamite freed them for our daily use.

Opposition to dynamite in the United States stopped on a January day in 1880. Early that morning a group of workmen, wearing mittens and mufflers and carrying picks and shovels, met in a flat open field near Gibbstown, New Jersey. There Repaupo Creek makes junction with the broad Delaware River, across from Chester, Pennsylvania.

The leader of the group, a tall, bearded figure in heavy overcoat, was Lammot du Pont. Through a devious maze of secret agreements, alliances, and ownerships, the Du Ponts controlled the manufacture and

sale of most of the gunpowder and black blasting powder made in the United States. Nobody had opposed
dynamite more bitterly than they.

Lammot du Pont swung a pick, pried loose a clod of
frozen earth, nodded, and his men went to work.

"We have begun here," he promised, "what will
some day be the biggest dynamite plant in America."

He could have said, with truth, the world.

The plant was named Repauno, the "*p*" of the creek
name being changed to "*n*" for greater euphony. The
nation's largest railroad, the Pennsylvania, sent an eminent chemist to Repauno to watch Du Pont men pitch
boxes of dynamite onto jagged rocks and set fire to the
sticks, as Nobel had done in Germany. The chemist's
decision was that, with proper precautions, the high
explosive could be carried as freight at less risk than
black blasting powder.

The big railroad, then others, lifted their bans.
Steamship companies quickly followed. Dynamite's
bootlegging days drew to an end.

The work of mixing the nitroglycerin with its cushioning material was still done with rakes and shovels
by hand. Chemicals were carried about in copper
buckets or in wheelbarrows, and men wound up their
day's work with violent headaches from the fumes.

Lammot du Pont set out to create at Repauno a new
type of plant, so fully mechanized that if an accident
should occur, machines only, not men, would suffer.
He built earthworks about each hazardous operation
to confine any explosion to that one area. He developed

a power-driven wheel mixer, had his engineers begin work on a machine that would fill, pack, and seal the cartridges. Precautions against any worker's carrying matches into the plant were of Spartan cast. Before going to work the men had to strip off all their clothes, walk through a channel of water up to their chins, then dress in fresh clothes provided them by the company.

Despite all the care at Repauno, somebody made a mistake in the nitrating house on March 29, 1884. Waving everybody back, Du Pont himself rushed into the house to try to correct the error. He was a second too late. A huge fuming vat exploded, burying Du Pont in the earthwork that confined the blast. Five others were killed by flying timbers and scraps of metal.

Other Du Ponts took over at Repauno. Later, in turn, three of Lammot's sons headed the Du Pont Company's steadily expanding interests. They made the manufacture of dynamite, of all high explosives, among the safest of all industrial occupations, setting standards that today are general throughout the explosives industry.

In 1954, Repauno ceased to be an explosive plant and was converted to chemicals, after having produced more than three billion pounds of dynamite and other explosives used chiefly in blasting. The largest of the Du Pont seven dynamite plants of today is located on the Potomac River, near Martinsburg, West Virginia. There mechanical robots, controlled from electric switchboards, turn out dynamite under heavy mounds of safeguarding concrete and earth.

But the distinction of operating the world's biggest dynamite plant is no longer the Du Ponts', or America's either. About 1935 that honor passed to a company known as African Explosives & Chemical Industries, Ltd., and to its mighty plant near Modderfontein, South Africa.

The passing is evidence of the new day of industry that is dawning over what once was the Dark Continent.

Chapter 10

THE BOTTLED GENIE

$\mathbf{D}$YNAMITE solved no problems for military men still befogged by smoke and grime, though as late as the Spanish-American War they hoped it might. The explosive did in guns what it did in hard rock: it blasted! Guns blew up in the faces of their crews.

Finally, American inventors developed cannon that were enormous pneumatic tubes forty feet long. An air pump filled a chamber in the base of the tube with highly compressed air, which became the firing charge. When the gunner pulled a lever, the air blew forth a shell loaded with dynamite and guncotton, after the principle that is now employed in air rifles.

Batteries of the huge air tubes were installed in New York harbor, at Hilton Head, South Carolina, and at San Francisco. The Navy built the "dynamite ship" U.S.S. *Vesuvius,* one of the wonders of the 1890's. The ship had, mounted on her bow, three monster air rifles which hurled shells weighing a thousand pounds each and containing six hundred pounds of dynamite and guncotton.

Because of the need to keep all three guns geared to the air compressor, they were mounted rigidly on the ship's deck. To aim the battery, the gunner aimed the ship by pointing its prow at the target. An electric storage battery inside each shell detonated the guncotton on impact, the guncotton detonated the dynamite.

Great things were expected of the *Vesuvius* when, in 1898, she was used in the attack of Santiago, Cuba. She had thirty missiles aboard, supposedly the most destructive ever made. They could either be hurled upon the Spanish defenses like artillery shells, or shot through the water as torpedoes to sink enemy ships.

The *Vesuvius,* however, had two weak points. Its air guns could shoot only a mile, whereas the enemy guns had ranges of more than three miles. The second hazard was that a single enemy shot might explode the ship's entire arsenal in one terrific blast of eighteen thousand pounds of high explosives loaded in its thirty big shells.

So handicapped, the American captain was forced to attack in the black of night, hoping to sneak in and out of the hostile harbor undetected by the Spanish forts. He had to aim his ship, and his guns, entirely by compass and with engines silent. After several attempts, discoveries by the enemy, and wild flights to escape bursting shells, the *Vesuvius* did manage at last to get off a salvo. The thunder of the dynamite shells shook the city.

But next morning the Spanish forts stood undamaged. Three holes in their stretch of green lawn were the sole results of the hair-raising adventure. After hearing all the facts, Congress decided to retire all dynamite guns, as well as the *Vesuvius,* to an inglorious page of history. Today dynamite is almost wholly an explosive of peace, of mining and construction. Its war uses are limited to demolition work, such as blowing up enemy bridges.

While the great air guns and the dynamite ship had been capturing newspaper headlines, to end with the fiasco at Santiago, discredited guncotton re-entered the military arena by way of a remarkable string of events dating over a half century or longer.

Even before Schönbein nitrated his wife's cotton apron in 1846, other seekers after a smokeless gunpowder had also nitrated cotton, wood pulp, and all sorts of other materials that are chemically known as cellulose. But their nitrated celluloses had merely burned, not exploded, and they were given the unexciting class name of pyroxylin, a word coined from the Greek that means "firewood."

Some of the pyroxylins burned mildly and some burned fiercely, but none seemed to have any practical use. Until the invention of guncotton, they were almost ignored, or treated as chemical curiosities.

But in 1847 a way was devised to determine the nitrogen content of guncotton and the pyroxylins. They were found to be as alike chemically as cups of tea to which sugar has been added, a spoonful to one cup, two spoonfuls to a second, three to a third. Guncotton was in the three spoonfuls class: it was trinitrated.

This new knowledge opened a boundless field to

guided experimenting with nitrated cellulose. It was boundless because cellulose comprises the fibrous cellular structure of plants and trees, which makes it an inexhaustible source of carbon. It was guided because it was now possible to experiment with various degrees of nitration, from weak to medium to strong, from harmless to violent, and know what was in progress.

A Boston medical student, J. Parkers Maynard, experimented with chemicals as a diversion from hospital rooms and textbooks. One evening he took a weakly nitrated cotton pyroxylin and treated it with a solution of ether and alcohol, two common hospital supplies. His resulting compound was a clear, syrupy liquid.

By odd coincidence, a French poet and amateur chemist named Ménard produced an identical liquid by the same method at about the same time. Ménard, however, did nothing about his discovery; Maynard did.

He put a drop of the liquid on his hand. The drop spread out, and the warmth of the skin soon dried it into a smooth, tough, pliable film. The film was hard to wash off; it resisted both water and soap.

Wounds, cuts, and bandages were a part of young Maynard's routine, so he tried painting some of the stuff over a cut on his hand. The film proved an excellent protector, and was easier to apply and less bothersome than a bandage. The cut healed readily.

Maynard called his find collodion, and in 1848 reported it to medical circles. He never dreamed that his simple invention would start revolutions in the world's work, its play, its dress, and its wars beyond all the imaginings of the most farsighted men.

Soon drug manufacturers were turning out vials of collodion, or "new skin," by the thousands, for use in home, office, and shop. The tiny bottles went the world around. As one looks back today, it seems that corked inside an astonishing number of the bottles was an invisible genie who inspired men to think of other uses for collodion.

An English chemist, Frederick Scott-Archer, was annoyed by the crude methods then followed in making photographic plates. In 1850 he coated some plates with collodion film and started the struggling photographic industry on the road to greatness. The modern marvels of motion pictures, tape recorders, even cellophane film, all trace their origins back to that experiment in London.

And it was but the beginning of a mighty sequence. If, in 1863, you had poked about a printing plant in Albany, New York, where a typesetter named John Wesley Hyatt was working, you would have found a vial of the collodion there. Hyatt swore by this "new skin" and always kept a bottle on a shelf in the washroom.

He was twenty-six, a butcher's son, and a student of much of the writing that he set in type. This made him aware of many things, among them the need for a substitute for ivory, which was becoming scarce and expensive. A prize of $10,000 had been offered to anyone who might find a replacement for ivory in making billiard balls.

With a fellow printer, James Brown, as helper, the young typesetter set out to win that prize. His workshop was a shed in the rear of Mrs. MacTavish's boardinghouse where he lived. In their spare time, he and Brown built a crude machine in which, by applying heat and pressure, they hoped to mold billiard balls out of pulverized wood and glue.

The scheme was working poorly when, at the printshop, Hyatt skinned a knuckle. Going to the washroom for his "new skin" he found the vial overturned and its contents spilled. The collodion had formed into a hard dry blob on the shelf. He stared at the blob in excitement. It resembled ivory! Or with a touch of the right color added it would!

Thereafter Hyatt forgot pressed wood. He talked with a local chemist and borrowed some textbooks. He learned that an English experimenter, Parkes, already had made an imitation of ivory by combining collodion and camphor, but the imitation cost almost as much as ivory because of the amount of ether and alcohol Parkes had used. Undismayed, the two printers began molding collodion and camphor in their machine in the shed.

They deviated from Parkes' tack. Using much less ether and alcohol, they compensated for that loss by using heat and high-pressure to hasten the drying process in. the mold. They never did make a satisfactory billiard ball, but they did better. They invented celluloid and so began the plastics industry, today a giant that molds and presses plastics of many kinds and thousands of uses.

To the original pyroxylin or nitrocellulose, Maynard had brought ether and alcohol, Parkes had contributed camphor, and Hyatt's ingenuity had added heat and high-pressure to the processing methods.

In France, Count Hilaire de Chardonnet was a student of these advances as well as a chemist of imagination. The luster and smoothness of celluloid made him think, not of ivory, but of silklike textile fibres that would be immune to the diseases that plagued silk worms. Soon he had an original idea.

His idea was to force liquid collodion under high-pressure through a tiny hole, about the diameter of a small sewing needle, until it squirted into a warm air drying chamber in the form of a continuous spray. The spray should solidify into a filament by this plan, the silky fiber of his vision.

De Chardonnet worked five years perfecting a machine, the heart of which was its "spinnerette." This was a disc about the size of a small silver coin, into which he had bored several tiny holes. Thus, his spinnerette spun a number of filaments at once, which were then intertwined to form a thread.

He announced his invention in 1889. The first use to be made of his lustrous cellulose threads was carbon filaments for incandescent gas lamps. But his "Chardonnet Silk" was destined for a grander role. It was the first man-made textile fiber, later called rayon, the forerunner of today's synthetic fibers industry.

Meanwhile, a vial of collodion had found its way into the medicine cabinet of Alfred Nobel. He was then living in Paris. Angry because of the many kinds of dynamite that were competing with his own all over the world, he was seeking a new kind of dynamite that would be superior to all.

The year is now 1873. Nobel had tried combining nitroglycerin and guncotton but was fearful of such an explosive union in daily use. Working in his laboratory late one evening, he cut his finger on the glass of a broken retort. He painted the cut with collodion, watched it dry, and went to bed.

But the finger was painful and kept him awake. Over and over his mind reviewed the day's work which had netted nothing more than an ugly cut. Abruptly he sat up in bed, alert. His thought centered on the cut, then on the collodion filmed over it. The film suggested, as if it spoke aloud, that it held the key to his unsolved puzzle. He got into his dressing gown, lighted a lamp, and with the robe flaring about his bare legs fairly ran down to his laboratory.

Just after dawn, the usual start of Nobel's workday, his assistant arrived. Nobel startled him with the cry, "I've got it!" The bent, bearded little man in night robe and cap held up a stone bowl in which was a pale yellow substance that looked like jelly. It was a compound of nitroglycerin and collodion, and Alfred Nobel's third great invention: *blasting gelatin.*

Blasting gelatin, or gelatin dynamite, is nearly as waterproof as rubber. For blasting in wet bore holes in rock, or underwater in deepening rivers and harbors, the gelatin dynamites are without a rival. Made today in a wide range of grades to suit any type of rock, the hundred per cent grade is the most powerful nonmilitary explosive in existence.

However, it was Hyatt's celluloid, and not blasting gelatin, that stirred military interest in collodion and the pyroxylins. By 1880 men were wearing celluloid collars, and women celluloid ornaments. Children's toys were being pressed from celluloid. Bone was being pushed out of the button market by this plastic of nitrocellulose base.

"Why," asked the generals, "if guncotton can be made safe enough for babies' rattles, can't somebody make it safe enough for war?"

The problem was to nitrate the cellulose to the exact explosive point desired, or somewhere midway between toys and Schönbein's wrecker. To Europe's armies, the need was urgent.

Rapid-fire cannon of long-range; repeating, or magazine rifles; machine guns; all awaited only a smokeless gunpowder to make them the standard weapons. The army that got the powder first, and rearmed to it, might dominate Europe, the world!

So the future of nations was in the scales. It is one

of history's monumental ironies that the tipping of the
scales depended upon adapting to war the unwarlike
inventions of a medical student and a printer. An
added irony was that the two were Americans, though
the United States appeared the least concerned over
the outcome of what quickly became a race.

Turkey moved first. A few of her troops were armed
with repeating rifles in the Russo-Turkish War of
1877-78. Germany moved next. Foreseeing early discovery of a cleanly-burning explosive for guns, and
wishing to be ready for it, she equipped her entire
Army with repeating rifles in 1884. Europe was now
alive with whispered rumors.

That same year the French Army tested in secrecy
an explosive labeled *Poudre B.* Its inventive genius
was a physicist, Paul Vielle. A new science was in the
arena of war. Before the end of 1885 France was also
rearmed, and to a purpose. *Poudre B* was the long-
sought smokeless gunpowder!

It was celluloid in uniform, an explosive upgrading
of Maynard's "new skin" and Hyatt's toys, a plastic
that could be molded into sheets, rods, or tubes, and
then machined into pellets or grains suitable for any
type of firearm from pistol to huge cannon.

Poudre B did not blast, nor did it merely burn like
celluloid, which people had learned to keep away from
lighted matches. It was nitrated to serve a precise explosive purpose which was to push or propel a shot
from a gun barrel at high velocity. It introduced a
new class of explosives, the propellants, intended only

for firing guns. Their superiority over black powder in firearms is as great as that of electricity over oil in lamps.

The race was now to overtake France. Bearing no nation's banner, in 1887 Alfred Nobel created Ballistite. It was a revised form of his blasting gelatin, in which he reduced the amount of nitroglycerin and increased the collodion until in place of a jelly he, too, had a plastic. This he produced in sheets which could be formed into ribbons, rods, tubes, or grains as desired.

Nobel offered his invention to Great Britain, Germany, and Italy. By 1888 the German repeating rifles were firing a slightly modified Ballistite, and Italy adopted it under the name of Filite. The British, with ideas of their own, borrowed the principle of the spaghetti-making machine to produce a powder in strings or cords, which they called Cordite.

Belgium turned to a modified *Poudre B*. Russia, in 1896, rearmed around a still further modified *Poudre B* of its own. As for the Army and Navy of the United States, they fought the Spanish-American War of 1898 with a brown variant of the old black gunpowder.

The twentieth century opened with every great power of Europe armed with the rapid-firing weapons that "clean" gunpowder made possible. Outwardly, armaments appeared to be fairly equal, with no nation in a position to dominate; the balance of power, and peace, seemed secure. If Germany had more machine guns and heavy cannon, as she did, that appeared to be simply a matter of choice, and no ill omen. France and

Great Britain, as their choice, had more light field artillery.

Actually, however, the equality in armaments was far from real. Gunpowder's successors were the products of a new type of inventive effort, one that had been growing bit by bit with the knowledge of chemistry and physics. The heart of the new effort was the research laboratory. Just as the old gunpowder had added mines, mills, foundries, steam power, railroads, all that summed up as mechanical industry to war's weapons, so the new explosives had added industrial science on a mass production scale. Then, as today, it was the mightiest weapon yet known to war.

As Europe's new armies drilled and maneuvered during the war games around 1910, the world outside Germany seemed totally unaware of the basic change in industry that lay behind the changes in powder and guns. Research, as an inventive tool, was still left to lone workers, and so mostly to inspiration and chance, in France, Britain, Russia, America, everywhere except in the nation on the Rhine. In Germany alone big central chemical and physics laboratories had been built and equipped, able scientists recruited to man them, ample funds set aside to finance the first organized efforts at invention. As a result, Germany had become the organic chemical center of the world, a citadel of scientific power such as existed nowhere else, and never had existed before.

How Germany gained that master position is one of the strangest of all of history's tales. She won her mastery largely by England's default — at least, Germany need not to have advanced unchallenged. Few, if any, defaults have led to consequences so vast. Again we must look back, in this case three centuries.

You will recall the Rev. Dr. Clayton, the discoverer of coal tar, who liked to amuse his friends by setting fire to a jet of coal gas as he pressed the "Spirit" from a pinhole in a bladder. Much later, England developed the uses of coal gas on large scale, and became the largest producer of coal tar.

At first the black, sticky stuff seemed of no value except in making tar paper for roofing. But by 1825 the chemists were exploring its mysteries with a new fervor. They separated benzene from coal tar and got both a cleaning fluid and nitrobenzene, an explosive. They identified naphthalene as a coal tar chemical, and so marked coal tar as a close relative of petroleum. Lampblack from the tar furnished printing inks and shoe polish; creosote went to work as a preservative for posts, poles, and railway ties. England led the way in these experiments.

An outstanding coal tar researcher in Europe of the mid-century was the German chemist, August Wilhelm von Hofmann. He was persuaded by the German-born Prince Consort of Queen Victoria to come to England, where he was made the Director of the Royal College of Chemistry in London. Among his pupils the German chemist found a remarkable youth, William Henry Perkin, whom he made his assistant. By that act he set a new pivot for world history.

Perkin was seventeen, the son of a London builder.

At home in a little laboratory he had fixed up, he experimented with Von Hofmann's ideas during the evening. The German had linked coal tar with indigo, the dark-blue natural dye that England's textile industry got from India. The link was aniline, a colorless light oil that smelled like wine. Aniline could be separated both from indigo and from benzene.

The inference was clear: aniline from coal tar, Perkin reasoned, must contain the same magic properties as the aniline yielded by a tropical plant. It should hold the first dye color to be created by chemical means!

So young Perkin worked with coal tar aniline. On being exposed to air it hardened and became brown. It burned readily, giving off a smoky flame. He got various results as he tried one chemical treatment and another, knowing that success in research is the sum of many failures. Early in 1856, as he neared his eighteenth birthday, he made one of the towering discoveries of chemical science: a dye of a delicate reddish purple color like that of lilacs, which he called mauve.

The youth quit school. With the help of his father and brother, he set up the first coal tar dye plant at Greenford Green, England. Later, he developed the red dye alizarin, formerly obtained only from madder roots. His work indicated that in coal tar was a mine of wealth that nature had created over the ages in converting decaying vegetation into coal.

But Perkin's attempts to convince England of that fact failed dismally. His plant at Greenford Green closed down permanently about 1874, a losing venture in competition with natural dyes from India, a British possession that demanded British support.

Likewise, Von Hofmann failed to arouse England by his warning that in the mastery of coal tar chemicals was an open road to a new kind of might in many fields, that dyes were but the first milepost on that road. After nineteen years in London, Von Hofmann returned to Germany to preach his creed to attentive audiences at the University of Berlin, and to organize the great German Chemical Society.

England knighted Perkin in 1906, a year before he died, but by then the dyes industry that he had founded was almost wholly Germany's. Soon that loss was brought home to Britain and the world by World War I.

Germany's industrial scientific research system was strongly developed by 1914, and it revolved about coal tar dyes. She had a monopoly of three-fourths of the coal tar dyes in world use, and supplied the coal tar "intermediates" for the remainder. In England, when the war paralyzed commerce, dyes were soon lacking even for flags and uniforms. In the United States, the government did not have enough dyes to print its postage stamps and paper money. All over the world, the textile, paper, paint, leather, and ink industries were disorganized by the absence of German dyes.

That was not all. Germany controlled the supply of many medicinal drugs, anesthetics, and disinfectants upon which physicians and hospitals had grown dependent. These also had been developed from coal tar, and had no substitutes.

But it was on the battlefields of Europe that Britain and her allies were made most aware of her default forty years earlier.

The Allies had prepared for a war of maneuvers in the open with occasional battles that might last a few days each. That was why they had emphasized light field artillery in their armaments, and had laid up stores of shrapnel shells which burst in the air with showers of small shot to harass troops in the field. The Allies were totally unprepared for the warfare in trenches and dugouts that actually took place.

Germany was not! Her army of chemists and physicists behind the fighting front prepared her.

Germany had large-caliber guns of long range — the largest, known as Big Bertha, had a range of seventy-five miles. The long-range guns tore gaps in the Allies' trench systems with explosive shells of a destructiveness unknown before. Made of steel and designed to penetrate earthworks, dugouts, and concrete emplacements, the shells then detonated with a disruptive violence of 2,250,000 pounds to a square inch.

The new explosive was so immune to shock that it could be handled safely under practically all conditions met in war. It could be melted, poured into shells, and cast like iron or other solids. The German chemists had built plants to produce it by the thousands of tons.

It was TNT, or trinitrotoluene!

Toluene is derived from benzene, the coal tar "crude" from which Perkin had made his first dye fifty-eight years before the war and had been given its name by Von Hofmann in London.

On one front alone during those grim weeks of 1914-15, the Allies seemed to hold the advantage. Germany was shut off from the world's major source of saltpeter, the ancient ingredient of gunpowder upon which all explosives still depended for their nitrogen.

The saltpeter beds of India, long the chief supplier of nitrates for explosives, had been exhausted. The only source left that was large enough to sustain an output of explosives on the scale of the war was in Chile, on the far west coast of South America. And Britain commanded the Chilean nitrate lanes with her fleet.

Efforts to obtain nitrogen from the air, as Henry Cavendish had done by using an electric spark, were ruled out for Germany. She lacked the water power to provide enough cheap electricity for such a task. The Allied leaders confidently expected the war to end just as soon as Germany's store of saltpeter was exhausted and her supply of explosives ran out.

They overlooked the organized German chemists.

The science built up by coal tar turned back to coal. Chemists added water and air and produced nitrogen "fixed" in the form of ammonia by the tank car load. The method, developed by a chemist named Fritz Haber, totally changed the world picture on nitrates, and changed it overnight.

Chile's natural nitrate beds suddenly belonged to a dying age. Germany's nitrates from the atmosphere relegated saltpeter to history's museum along with the sword, the bow, and the war club.

Chapter 11

BOMBS FOR PEACE?

AT first, people wondered if World War I were not a nightmare. By 1915 they wondered if the enemies of Germany could survive. Supreme in explosives, automatic arms, heavy guns, submarines, and above all in science, the German war machine seemed to have reached the pinnacle of might.

However, fourteen nations, including the United States, lined up behind France, Britain, and Russia. The Allies mobilized more than 42,000,000 men against about half of that number. In spite of the new chemical wizardry, Germany was beaten after four years, by overwhelming physical force.

More than 8,500,000 were killed or died. That was 1700 times the dead of America's Civil War, the most destructive war fought with black gunpowder. When we consider that more than half of the dead of 1861-65 died of disease, not in battle, the 1700 is doubled.

France, or what was left of her, rebuilt her razed towns and villages, many of them so leveled that their ruins were lost among the weeds. The nations saw to it that the rows upon rows of white crosses in the new military cemeteries were kept white, those of friend and foe alike. Memorials in granite marked the bloodiest battlefields.

Meanwhile, the nations prepared for the next war, and in 1939 it came.

World War II dwarfed the first debacle. Both sides were now reinforced by great chemical industries. Smokeless powder was now so improved that machine guns were to attain firing speeds of seven hundred shots per minute. TNT was no longer the super destroyer: cyclotol and torpex, developed from coal tar, were of twice its violence. A new family of coal tar high explosives had been added to armaments.

All explosives were now produced on mammoth scale. The outputs of American plants alone exceeded, in tons, the total powder consumption in pounds of both sides in the Civil War.

An incredible new horror was revealed in August, 1945. The first atomic bombs were dropped by American war planes on Japan. Each A-bomb had an explosive force equal to twenty thousand tons of TNT. In minutes, the Japanese losses from two bombs were larger by several times than the combined losses of three days of hard fighting in the Battle of Gettysburg. One bombing squadron packed more destruction than had Napoleon's Grand Army. Three A-bombs — three — were capable of more thorough wreckage than all the TNT that was produced in America during the nineteen months in which the United States was a belligerent in World War I.

World War II ended with some 31,000,000 dead.

And the dead now included old men, women, and children, the sick, the blind, and the crippled scores of miles behind the fronts. The total money cost was $1,400,000,000,000, a sum too stupendous for the mind to grasp. Much of Europe was a shambles.

There was a pause, but only a pause. The race for more terrible explosives was resumed at a greater speed. Former allies became enemies, and West faced East in the cold war of today's headlines. The hydrogen bomb was developed. The A-bomb became its blasting cap, even as TNT had become the exploder of the A-bomb.

No word existed in any language to convey the explosive force of the H-bomb, so it was necessary to invent a new word of measure: the megaton. A megaton represents the concentrated violence of one million tons of TNT, or of fifty A-bombs combined into one.

Today our new warriors of science are working to perfect war missiles that might be hurled halfway around the earth, each carrying *ten* megatons of disaster by explosive action alone. Scientists are unable to agree on the extent to which their bombs will destroy all kinds of life or affect the health of future generations by radioactive pollution of the atmosphere.

They do agree upon a horror beyond ordinary belief. The United States and Russia are now able to launch bombing attacks upon each other in unison, which within hours would treble the losses suffered by all nations combined in *both* recent world wars!

In short, yesterday's debacles have become skirmishes. "Entirely realistic" was one famous expert's comment on a recent official estimate of 49,000,000 American dead from one "moderate-sized" nuclear attack of continental dimensions. Another authority added that the contamination of exposed foodstuffs and crops would seriously threaten the lives of all survivors.

One asks: Have the electronic robots of the missile laboratories become the soul and conscience of modern man? For stored today in American and Russian arsenals, awaiting release at a signal, are explosives of a greater destructive power than probably was combined in all the weapons of all man's wars since the Stone Age.

A nuclear war, should there be one, could be, in grim truth, the war that would end all war, and life as we know it. The peace of our time has become a peace of suicidal dread. In the United States armament has become the nation's chief business, one that eats up more Federal revenue than all other government activities put together. For the first time in our history, bombs take precedence over bread.

Yet there are entries, too, on the credit side of the ledger for gunpowder's successors, and nowhere are those entries so marked as in the United States.

Prior to 1914, America contributed little to the upgrading of explosives or to the broad advance of the material sciences. Collodion and celluloid, the inventions of a student and a printer, did no more than supply two links in a chain forged in Europe. Conversely, gunpowder had helped Americans win the

West, and dynamite had blazed trails to greatness as an industrial power.

America's bent was mechanical. Our most notable war inventions were the Colt revolver, the Winchester repeating or magazine rifle, machine guns, the submarine, and ironclad warships. Among other advances in mechanics, we had contributed the cotton gin, harvesting machines, telegraph, telephone, electric lamp, and airplane.

Science, as an arm of industry and a weapon of war, was almost unknown in the United States when, early in the century, the thunder of TNT over Europe awoke us to a new order of inventive effort. Suddenly the country appeared to be almost defenseless, and as opposed to science-armed Germany it was. Among all the pivotal discoveries made in chemistry and physics, Americans could be credited with only four. We were especially deficient in coal tar chemistry, the backbone science of the German war machine: American coal tar plants could count only 528 employees, and they looked to Germany for essential supplies.

Our colleges were strangely indifferent toward the teaching of organic chemistry and physics, for the reason that the public was indifferent. Students who wished to take advanced courses in the two sciences had to go to Germany for them. Fortunately a number had done so. Even in medicine we were deficient; advanced medical students had to study in Europe.

Then the awakening. German dyes became unobtainable, and America threatened to become a nation in gray. Every sickroom felt the lack of German drugs; even aspirin was scarce. The new explosives, then poison gases, then the fixation of air nitrogen, proclaimed that science was the new master power.

That fact became more obvious as the country suffered new shortages in the home supply. Our farms depended on Germany for potash, on Chile for nitrates. Though the rise of the automobile had made us the largest user of rubber — now, too, a military necessity — not a pound of rubber was grown at home.

All nations allied against Germany felt their lack of organized science, while the Germans seemed able to perform wonders at will as the war pinches tightened. Gunpowders based on Nobel's Ballistite contained nitroglycerin, and it pitted or eroded the bores of big guns. German researchers ended that costly fault by lining gun bores with a new nickel-steel alloy. It was the hard, bright metal that we know as stainless steel, and as expressive as TNT of the new order that was taking over.

"Organized science — research!" swelled into a battlecry on every Allied home front.

A new goal, national self-sufficiency in raw materials, was introduced to statecraft and industry alike. Leaders warned that political independence now hinged on economic independence, which hinged in turn largely on organic chemistry.

As we regard this abrupt turn in thinking created by World War I, and imagine the headlines, the speeches in Parliament and in Congress, it is instructive to look back to Friar Bacon. What he began in a monk's cell was now to be expanded into a major function of industry and government. The modern nation in arms, born in the French Revolution, was no longer complete without its army of scientists.

In Britain, the government joined hands with private capital to found Imperial Chemical Industries, a great new chemical company capable of vying with the German chemical cartel. France made outright grants of public funds to new chemical concerns and freed them from paying taxes. Italy and Czechoslovakia set up national chemical trusts. When the Soviets seized control in Russia, chemists and physicists, scorned by the Czars, became members of the Communist elite. Scientific research was made a primary function of the Soviet state.

In the United States, German patents on file in Washington were turned over to American companies. German-owned plants were seized and sold to Americans. A wall of high tariffs was thrown up to keep out Europe's chemical products after the war and thus leave the field open to home manufacturers.

By 1919 some $200,000,000 was invested in coal tar dyes plants by 118 American companies. An initial outlay of $300,000,000 was made to expand the teaching of chemistry and physics in schools and colleges. Scientists were brought in from Germany to help in the nationwide surge forward.

Nothing sums up the movement so strikingly as the

transformation of the Du Pont Company, which since 1802 had produced possibly two thirds of America's explosives. As the war ended, the great Du Pont plants employed 100,000 persons. The company might easily have reverted to its prewar status as a maker of explosives only, employing about 6000. But the Du Ponts led the new organic chemical revolution.

Capital of $60,000,000 for chemistry was authorized as early as 1915. Another $400,000,000 was set aside between 1920 and 1939. Other companies already engaged in chemical work were acquired by mergers and exchanges of stock.

Note, now, the Du Pont expansion into an array of unwarlike products that yet are the chemical cousins of smokeless powder and most high explosives:

1915 — pyroxylin plastics
1917 — coal tar dyes
1920 — rayon
1923 — cellophane
1924 — photographic film
1924 — "fixed" air nitrogen

The plastics of 1914 and the rayon of 1920 were but crude beginnings when compared to their present-day descendants. Eighteen years of work went into dyes and related chemicals before that sector of the new front was mastered. But the risks of capital brought big rewards to Du Pont and sweeping changes in the nation.

The mass production of automobiles, furniture, of everything using paint was held up by the slowness of paint to dry. In wet weather thousands of cars were impounded in drying rooms, often for days. Sometimes it required as many as twenty-two separate coats of primers, glazes, and other finishes to turn out a fine car or a piano. Then, the finish on cars had to be renewed in about six months, that of the piano was as quickly watermarked and cracked.

In 1923, the Du Pont chemists introduced the first quick-drying and durable finish, Duco laquer. It was the only important change in paints and varnish that had been made since the Pyramids were built. And Duco traced its lineage through smokeless gunpowder and celluloid to Maynard's collodion or "new skin." It was now a new skin for metal.

As an aside, another descendant of collodion soon made it possible to cement two sheets of plate glass together into a sandwich form. So cemented, the glass did not shatter in an accident. It was safety glass, now standard in automobiles.

Onward went the Du Pont chemists.

America's fears of being shut off by war from the Far East, and natural rubber, had grown to monumental size by the mid-1920's. Led by Thomas Edison, scientists tried to obtain rubber from such common home plants as goldenrod and artichokes. The chemists, however, an eye on the German record, turned to coal. Once more they read Von Hofmann's prophecy, made in London a half century earlier, that in the mastery of coal's chemistry were economic and military might.

In 1931, from coal, limestone, and salt, by way of the fiery gas, acetylene, chemists gave America its first synthetic or chemically-made rubber, *neoprene*. Neoprene was the forerunner of a class of synthetic rubbers and rubber processing chemicals that today give our automobile tires ten times the life of 1914 tires, and also give America rubber independence in war. TNT must share in the credit for that feat.

Again in 1931, and again using coal, but this time combined with water and air, Du Pont produced the first nylon. As its three main raw materials are those of the nitrogen fixation plants, nylon is a chemical kin of ancient saltpeter. It made its bow in women's stockings, but in World War II nylon went to war as the replacement for Japanese silk in parachutes.

By then Du Pont was our largest manufacturer of explosives and chemicals. Some ten thousand products were listed in the company's order books, and ninety per cent of them were not explosives. But they all stemmed from the common sources of wood, cotton, coal, water, and air. And sulphur, the brimstone of ancient gunpowder, was an important element in their processing.

Moreover, five other big chemical companies pressed at Du Pont's heels, and behind them an industry numbering more than seven thousand separate chemical concerns. The nation stood second to none in organized science when Pearl Harbor spelled war.

You may name today almost any man-made thing that you will, from skyscrapers to shoes, from bridges to bread, and the new chemistry has improved it in some way, and possibly added months to its life span of service. Most important, the industry foretold by Friar Bacon has joined with medicine in adding years to the life spans of tens of millions of people as well — and explosives must share in that credit.

Americans were only mildly aware, as our century opened, of the crying need for better sanitation, pure water, germfree foodstuffs. They only vaguely knew the dangers in fly-borne diseases. They did not become acutely aware of how antiquated was the average food store until after the great chemical awakening, and a paralleling reorganization of medical education. Nowadays it seems unbelievable that only thirty-five years ago methods of handling foods had changed little since America's colonial times. Open bins and barrels and fly-infested counters were the usual dispensers.

In 1923 came cellophane. It was cellulose in still another guise, one now so common that the transparent, sparkling film has become as much a part of America's daily life as newspapers or ham and eggs. Cellophane wrappings, first of candies, then of other foods, were soon joined by waxed paper, tinfoil, cardboard boxes, and cartons of all kinds. They created the packaging industry and ended what now is known in food circles as the cracker barrel age. Modern sanitation became standard in retail food stores.

Meanwhile, agriculture underwent changes in methods of growing food crops, ways older than history, and it was "fixed" nitrogen from the air that led the upheaval. From time immemorial farmers had relied upon stable manure to supply nitrogen, the growth fertilizer, to their fields. Intensive cultivation over many generations depleting the soils, plus the increasing population to be fed, made nitrogen, by 1914, essential to the continued growth of nations.

How essential this fertilizer had become may be understood better if we make a quick survey. The widespread industrialization that had started with steam power had drawn young men by the millions from the farm to towns and cities. Instead of ninety per cent of Americans, for example, living on farms as in colonial days, ninety per cent were destined by 1914 to be living in urban communities. That meant one farmer had to produce the food formerly grown by nine farmers.

Of course, the invention of new farm machinery was an important beginning toward solving the increasing farm problem. Introduction of the gasoline motor was another boon, bringing to farmers the tractor and farm truck. But at the same time the tractor, truck, and automobile doomed the farm horse, and in so doing sharply diminished the manure supply just when a larger supply was imperative.

It was a time of increasing specialization in every

type of work, farming not excepted. On the great plains of the American West, wheat had become the special crop, or perhaps it was corn. Grain farms tended to have fewer and fewer animals. In time they were to become completely mechanized operations. The old stables were to vanish except on dairy farms. Dairymen specialized; more and more of them replaced the old cow stables and barnyards with milking sheds and let their cows roam over broad pastures except for the brief twice daily milkings.

As these trends developed, men who looked ahead began to wonder where the nitrogen supply, so vital to fertilization, was going to come from in the future to meet the rapidly increasing need for it. Some alarmists, recognized authorities, foresaw such a depletion of the soil that millions of people would be on half rations, and other millions would starve. India's saltpeter beds had been exhausted, a fact that pointed to the eventual fate of Chile's nitrate beds.

As we know, the prophetic day of too little food never arrived in Europe or America, though it is the plight of some over-populated parts of Asia which have yet to put modern technology to work. Here, for a decade or more, farm storages have been bursting with food surpluses, and what to do with them is now the problem. American yields of wheat, corn, all kinds of crops, are larger per acre than when every plow was horse-drawn, when every farm was rich in manure to spread on its fields.

Nitrogen fertilizers, trainloads of them flowing from

the same chemical plants that simultaneously feed nitrogen to the explosives makers, are a primary reason for the crop surpluses. Chemists have also compounded new chemicals to reduce age-old crop losses from disease and insects, and to increase the fertility of seeds. A result is that Americans today are the best fed people in the world.

That fact brings us to a most substantial gain that may be credited to the influence of explosives. The average American of today lives longer than ever before, our youths are taller, broader of shoulder, bigger of chest. Since 1909, according to a recent study, the average life span of Americans has been increased by twenty-four years. Most of that gain was made during the past quarter century.

Generally, the awakening that was brought about in America by TNT led to an effort and national resolve that pushed us into the forefront as scientific innovators. Before 1914, American science trailed Europe's. Since 1914, of a total of forty major discoveries in chemistry and physics, Germany has made nine, Britain eight, France two, the United States twenty-one.

The atom-smashing theory evolved in 1919 was English in origin. The first cyclotron, or atom-smasher, was built in 1929 by an American.

One might ask if these attainments and many others that have stemmed from the new concept of organized science might not have come about if gunpowder had never been invented, if nature alone were still the source of all physical energy used in doing men's work and fighting men's wars. The only answer is that they came about as they did — that the thousand years of man-created explosive energy introduced changes more vast than all the changes made during a million years of energy supplied solely by wind, water, and muscle power.

War was old when gunpowder turned men's vision toward inventive fields not even dreamed of previously. Gunpowder did not create war. It and its progeny merely magnified war into a destroyer of world scope and stripped it of all glory.

And therein, if we look, may be found the largest credit in the ledger of explosives. For the first time, hope for profit is not a motive for war waged with the newest weapons. Even with TNT, the bold use of new weapons promised a reward worthy of the risk to the nation introducing them. That incentive exists no more.

All the latest bombs and missiles promise is destruction on so vast a scale that the victor, if any might survive, will face losses far greater than those of the worst defeated nation of any war of the past.

Perhaps the American war planes that shocked the world with the horrors of the A-bomb in 1945 exploded the mightiest of all forces for peace among men. After long ages, perhaps the H-bomb will end war forever as an institution.

Meanwhile, the peaceful mastery of the explosive atom promises a rich reward: exhaustless power to open unknown new realms of wealth for all of mankind.

Index

ABOUT THE AUTHOR

WILLIAM S. DUTTON became acquainted with explosives at first hand in World War I when he served eighteen months in France and Germany as an infantryman with the famed 42nd, or Rainbow, Division. In World War II he went with General Patton across France into Germany as a staff officer of the Third U.S. Army. Later he served as a member of the General Staff Corps under General Bradley, and with the European Theater General Board. He has ten battle stars, the Bronze Star medal, and the rank of lieutenant colonel to his credit.

Between wars he wrote widely for leading magazines and spent twelve years on the public relations staff of E. I. du Pont de Nemours & Company. While with Du Pont he saw explosives being made. After Pearl Harbor, he worked with Du Pont engineers to establish the huge military explosives plants that the company built and operated for the U. S. Government. This experience led to the Army's request that he re-enter the military service as a major.

Philadelphia-born William Dutton is, however, primarily a writer. It was for *American Magazine* that he first wrote on explosives in 1924. The article was "Wonders Performed with Dynamite." It was followed by a book on the Du Pont Company, published in 1942, and in 1949 by a series of five articles on the Du Ponts in *The Saturday Evening Post*.

Work on the history of America's greatest makers of explosives took him back to the French Revolution. From that point, he says, it seemed only logical to study explosives and their influences on the world from the very beginning. The result is this book.

With his wife, Joan Parry Dutton, also an author, William Dutton now lives in northern California, surrounded by giant oaks, woodpeckers, and books.